Bridge with Aunt Agatha

Bridge with Aunt Agatha
Technique without Tears

FREDDIE NORTH

faber and faber

First published in 1983
by Faber and Faber Limited
3 Queen Square London WC1N 3AU
Filmset by Wilmaset, Birkenhead
Printed in Great Britain by
Redwood Burn Ltd, Trowbridge, Wiltshire
All rights reserved

British Library Cataloguing in Publication Data

North, Freddie
    Bridge with Aunt Agatha
    1. Contract bridge
    I. Title
    795.41'5   GV1282.3

    ISBN 0-571-13012-7
    ISBN 0-571-13014-3 (Pbk)

Contents

Acknowledgements

I am indebted to *Bridge Magazine* for permission to include some material that has appeared in that excellent publication.

My thanks are also due to Gus Calderwood for his diligence in endeavouring to eradicate my analytical errors, and to Jeremy Flint for taking a friendly—almost avuncular—interest.

Foreword

Can you picture an Agatha as a winsome young thing with a mass of blonde curls and a come-hither smile? No, of course not. The Agathas of this world may be handsome, even striking, but they are seldom pretty and even more rarely *femmes fatales*. They are, however, formidable; and aunts of this name, with their legendary chilling looks, are notoriously awesome.

You might suppose that Aunt Agatha is a figment of Freddie's imagination. I thought so, too, until my curiosity got the better of me. I went, I saw and I was conquered. But I remain sceptical of Aunt Agatha's benign *alter ego*—although no amount of persuasion will induce me to put it to the test. Though a keen racegoer, I even shun Lingfield Park rather than risk a second confrontation. I am happy to rely upon Freddie's amusing recollections of his old aunt. You, too, dear reader, are doubly lucky. You can enjoy the fun of reading about Aunt Agatha without the fear of meeting her in the flesh.

JEREMY FLINT

Learn as though you'll live for ever.
Live as though you'll die tomorrow.

Introduction:
The Chief Characters

Like all bridge-players, Aunt Agatha enjoys winning. The only difference is that she is inclined to vent her feelings rather more volubly than most. Irascible, often illogical, and not given to suffering fools gladly, she can stop a conversation dead in its tracks with one of her looks. As one chemically-minded acquaintance once observed: 'Aunt Agatha is a master of the acid comment. Indeed, no ordinary piece of litmus paper would change colour at her touch—it would disintegrate.' Perhaps that is true, but beneath the rather chilling and formidable exterior are a kindly heart and an alert mind. Courageous, sometimes to the point of foolhardiness, Aunt Agatha plays a skilful game and is quite capable of winning a rubber or a match entirely on her own, regardless of the other members of the cast. Inevitably there are times when she is out of luck, and during one of these spells which seemed to be almost unending her arch rival and sometime friend Professor Issie Rabinovinski was heard to quote Napoleon's famous remark when the virtues of an up-and-coming young officer were extolled to him: 'I don't want to know whether he's good. Is he lucky?' This seemed a particularly apt quotation at the time, and it may not have been entirely coincidence that Issie's back-handed compliment was made outside the hearing of Aunt Agatha.

Issie is set in a very different mould to my aunt. Although a Professor of Psychology, he has never quite outgrown his fourth-form impishness, which takes a special delight in getting the better of Aunt Agatha at the bridge table. A fair player, bold and venturesome, who, like so many of his type, probably enjoys more success than his skill actually merits. Once asked to define bad luck he replied: 'It's like this. A chap wins half a girl in a raffle—and then finds he's got the half that talks. That's bad luck.'

Apart from myself and the occasional guest, Sally and Mildred make up the regular four. Sally is a fairly nondescript Mrs X that you meet in every bridge club in the country. A reasonable player, but you would hardly notice her unless somebody said, 'That is Mrs X.' Still, someone has to make up the numbers and Sally has been performing that role with great distinction for as long as I can remember. Mildred is a different kettle of fish. Nervous, hesitant, afraid of her own shadow and practically everything else as well—especially Aunt Agatha. Despite these obvious disadvantages she often produces the right bid, albeit with the confidence of an antelope attacking a tiger, and she is a competent player in her class if not asked to do anything out of the ordinary. Perhaps her worst fault is that she tends to play parrot bridge, relying on clichés and slogans rather than thinking for herself.

To digress for a moment, it is an accepted theory that the character of a man often changes dramatically when he is in the driving-seat of his car. The gentle, thoughtful and considerate representative of homo sapiens all too often becomes Mr Hyde, the monster, whose grotesque actions are completely out of character with his behaviour at home. A similar parallel applies in the case of many bridge-players for they, too, can go through a striking metamorphosis when seated round the green baize, clutching the devil's tickets.

In her own home, situated on the Sussex/Surrey borders, not far from Lingfield, Aunt Agatha is easily recognizable as the kindly old lady who has nothing but good in her heart. The pseudo-Tudor cottage with its fine old beams, the picturesque garden, so rich in scent and colour, and the enchanting waterfall at the end of the pergola sets a scene that positively shrieks of tranquility, gentleness and graceful living. But move my aunt to the bridge table and the transformation is at least equal to that of Dr Jekyll and Mr Hyde. Knowing the homely scene it is sometimes difficult to appreciate just what has happened as bridge gets underway and the cards start to weave their magic spells.

Mildred and Sally live in the same block of flats only three miles away from Aunt Agatha. Two very ordinary people living a very ordinary life.

Issie is more of a mystery. Superficially he seems to do nothing, but he spends a lot of time away from his bachelor apartment, also only a few miles from Aunt Agatha's cottage, and these trips are never accounted for with any degree of conviction. Aunt Agatha once confided to me that she thought he worked on something terribly secret for the Home Office, but if he does he never gives the slightest indication of it.

So much then for the star and supporting cast of this book. Not surprisingly, my aunt tends to dominate the scene. Do not think this strange. Indeed, it would be amazing if it were otherwise, for Aunt Agatha not only likes but *demands* the centre of attention.

Being the author of this book has given me one advantage that would surely be denied me if I happened to be back at the scene of the crime—I am able to have the last say. Such a role is almost unprecedented, for me or anyone else, so I had better make the most of it (and then, perhaps, leave the country for a while).

1. Aunt Agatha Plays Rubber Bridge

Sometimes to be a fly on the wall must be very exciting—and revealing. On one occasion I was even better placed. Invited for a weekend of what Aunt Agatha euphemistically described as 'friendly rubber bridge' I found myself partnering my aunt in the first rubber. It was not long before the balloon went up. This was Aunt Agatha's hand, sitting West:

♠ A 4
♡ 7 3
♢ A 9 8 7 6
♣ A 7 5 3

I wonder what you would make of the following bidding sequence:

S	W	N	E
(Issie)	(A. A.)	(Mildred)	(F. N.)
1 ♡	No	4 ♡	No
4 NT	No	5 ♣	No
7 ♡	?		

Aunt Agatha decided that she had heard enough and doubled—loudly. Mildred looked very perturbed at this development, but after several recounts and much heart searching she whispered, 'Redouble.' After three passes it was up to Aunt Agatha to find a lead. Any ideas?

It was clear to Aunt Agatha that the opponents had perpetrated a monumental nonsense. 'Even worse than usual,' as she described it to me later on. A trump, therefore, could not be far wrong. The ace of spades was tempting, but there seemed no good case for either minor-suit ace. Eventually a trump emerged, and so did thirteen tricks, gathered up by a highly elated Issie, who had made little attempt to conceal his obvious delight as he ruffed Aunt Agatha's aces one by one.

This was the full deal:

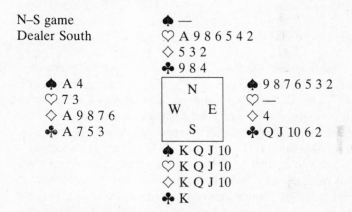

N–S game
Dealer South

♠ —
♡ A 9 8 6 5 4 2
♢ 5 3 2
♣ 9 8 4

♠ A 4
♡ 7 3
♢ A 9 8 7 6
♣ A 7 5 3

♠ 9 8 7 6 5 3 2
♡ —
♢ 4
♣ Q J 10 6 2

♠ K Q J 10
♡ K Q J 10
♢ K Q J 10
♣ K

Issie won the trump in the South hand; the king of spades came next and with that ace located it became a mere formality for him to re-enter his own hand with a trump, discard the losing diamonds, and then repeat the process with the king of diamonds so as to dispose of the club losers.

As you can imagine, there was quite a bit of backchat between Issie and Mildred over their bidding. Issie wanted to know why Mildred had not shown her ace in reply to Blackwood, while Mildred inquired meekly if Issie wasn't perhaps taking a slight chance in bidding the grand slam with all four aces missing. It seemed that Mildred had replied 5 ♣ because she wanted to dampen her partner's enthusiasm and was afraid that she had rather overdone it with her bid of 4 ♡. But her partner, with 21 points (and 100 honours) assumed that the reply must mean all four aces. Meantime, from Mildred's point of view, if partner could bid 7 ♡ missing the ace of trumps, which in any case she had denied holding, then this must surely be the time to redouble. However, it wasn't long before all was forgiven in the North-South corners, helped no doubt by the prospect of calculating the score. Curious what a soothing effect +3190 seems to have on a pair who have just experienced a muddle of gargantuan proportions.

THE LAST SAY

Issie was an ass! Although the correct reply to Blackwood holding four aces or no aces is 5 ♣, who would dream of raising to 4 ♡ with all the aces? Not even Mildred would make such a feeble offering. A further point he obviously overlooked in his excitement—if partner *has* all four aces, why not 7 NT? After all, 150 for honours is better than 100, and 7 ♡ may even be beaten on a first round ruff. As to the opening lead, Aunt Agatha was surely most unlucky. Neither the ace of diamonds nor the ace of clubs looks right; having thus eliminated the two leads to save the day, one can only accept the position with as much grace as possible.

A degree of sanity was restored to the proceedings when Mildred—now occupying the South seat traditionally reserved for declarer—played the next hand in game. What would you lead from this West hand, having listened to the following auction?

	S	W	N	E
	(Mildred)	(F. N.)	(Issie)	(A. A.)
♠ 3	—	—	—	1 NT*
♡ A Q 9 6 2	No	2 ♡	Dbl	No
◇ 8 6 3	3 ♣	No	4 ♠	No
♣ 6 5 4 3	No	No		
	* *12–14*			

Love all
Dealer East

♠ A 5 4 2
♡ 10 4
◇ A Q J 7
♣ K J 2

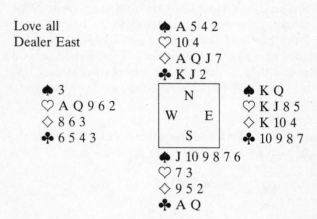

♠ 3
♡ A Q 9 6 2
◇ 8 6 3
♣ 6 5 4 3

♠ K Q
♡ K J 8 5
◇ K 10 4
♣ 10 9 8 7

♠ J 10 9 8 7 6
♡ 7 3
◇ 9 5 2
♣ A Q

I led a club, and that was that. Mildred drew one round of trumps, discarded a losing heart on the third round of clubs and eventually lost one heart, one diamond and one spade.

'Couldn't have made it on a heart lead,' burbled Mildred, and then, catching a withering look from Aunt Agatha, she added hastily, 'Not that they could have found it, of course.'

No doubt that last piece of soft soap was inspired by fear of Aunt Agatha, who is really nothing short of a master witherer when she turns her mind to it. Still, a successful defence is not easy to find. The ace and a small heart is not good enough, since that would leave East on lead. She can exit with a black suit, but declarer now cashes the ace of spades and three rounds of clubs, throwing a diamond, and then forces East back on lead for the final indignity—ruff and discard or lead into dummy's diamond tenace. Of course, I *could* have led a low heart at trick one, or, more realistically, cashed the ace of hearts and followed it with the queen before switching to a diamond. That would have been a smart defence.

THE LAST SAY

Issie and Mildred, flushed with success from their efforts in the previous rubber, combined well in the bidding. Issie's double merely said that he would have doubled 1 NT had West passed. It had no special bearing on the heart suit. Then Mildred showed some values, with game in mind if her partner's hand was suitable. It only needed me to louse up the lead and they were home.

Poor Aunt Agatha had been having rather a rough time of it up to now but the next hand gave her some consolation.

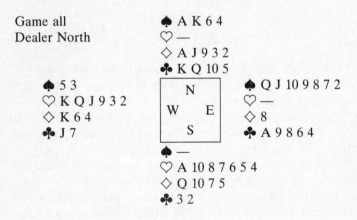

Game all
Dealer North

	♠ A K 6 4	
	♡ —	
	◇ A J 9 3 2	
	♣ K Q 10 5	

♠ 5 3

♡ K Q J 9 3 2

◇ K 6 4

♣ J 7

♠ Q J 10 9 8 7 2

♡ —

◇ 8

♣ A 9 8 6 4

♠ —

♡ A 10 8 7 6 5 4

◇ Q 10 7 5

♣ 3 2

The bidding:

S	W	N	E
(A. A.)	(Issie)	(F. N.)	(Mildred)
—	—	1 $\diamondsuit$	3 $\spadesuit$
4 $\heartsuit$	Dble	No	No
No			

Without putting too fine a point on it, nobody was left in any doubt as to Issie's intentions over 4 $\heartsuit$. The Professor's double was audibly for penalties. Lesser characters than Aunt Agatha would have retreated to 5 $\diamondsuit$, but that is hardly her style. Besides, she likes playing the hand.

The five of spades was led, which enabled Aunt Agatha to discard her losing clubs. Now the king of clubs forced the ace, declarer ruffing in hand. The queen of diamonds was covered by the king and ace, and then, somewhat hesitantly, Aunt Agatha tried the knave. But all was well when East discarded a spade. The nine of diamonds and queen of clubs were followed by a club which was ruffed by South and overruffed by West. So Issie had just one trick when he had to lead in this five-card ending:

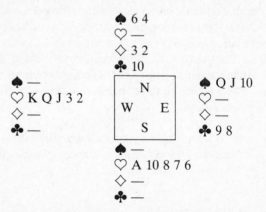

West was not a happy man, and you can see why. No amount of juggling will permit the defence to take more than two tricks unless South does something stupid. In fact Issie tried the effect of a small heart, but Aunt Agatha won with the six and calmly returned the seven. Issie won this trick with the knave but then had to lead away from K Q 3. Issie's three defensive tricks were the ♡ 9, ♡ J and ♡ Q. Issie looked quite stunned by the turn of events.

'You know, Mildred, I had the king, queen, jack, nine to six hearts,' he said incredulously.

'Shouldn't double until you get the goodies,' interrupted Aunt Agatha, thoroughly enjoying the situation. 'You know, my intuition told me that I was going to make this contract, otherwise I would have bid five diamonds.'

'Intuition indeed!' snorted Issie. 'Somebody once defined intuition as something that enables a woman to contradict a man before he has uttered a word.'

'Jealousy doesn't become you, Issie,' said Aunt Agatha. 'Help yourself to a drink and you'll feel better.'

THE LAST SAY

Although Aunt Agatha played this hand with her customary skill, one cannot help feeling that her bravery exceeded her wisdom, especially after Issie's ear-splitting double. It is true that a diamond contract requires careful handling by North, but in practice he is likely to come to twelve tricks. Furthermore, a club lead against 4 ♡—although improbable, I admit—would have given declarer no chance.

We didn't have to wait long—about half a vodka later—for a hand that can best be described as a chapter of accidents all round.

Game all
N–S+60
Dealer West

♠ A 9 5 4 3
♡ J 7 3
♢ A 5 4 2
♣ 4

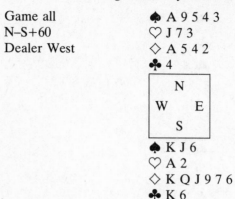

♠ K J 6
♡ A 2
♢ K Q J 9 7 6
♣ K 6

The bidding:

S	W	N	E
(A. A.)	(Mildred)	(F. N.)	(Issie)
—	4 ♣	No	No
4 ♢	5 ♣	5 ♢	No
No	No		

Mildred led the ace of clubs, East contributing the eight, and followed with the queen of clubs. Not being mean, or foolish, Aunt Agatha ruffed with the ace of diamonds while East discarded the ten of hearts. What now?

Aunt Agatha decided that she could easily afford an immediate spade finesse. After all, East probably had the queen—nine of West's cards were already accounted for—and even if West won with the queen of spades the suit might still be good for one discard. Without further ado she led a small spade from dummy and inserted the knave. But West ruffed and led the king of hearts. Perhaps it is time to look at the full hand:

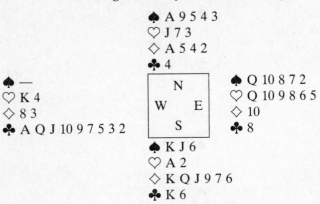

From the moment West ruffs the knave of spades the defence must prevail—assuming they keep their heads. The king of hearts is taken by the ace and trumps run to the following position:

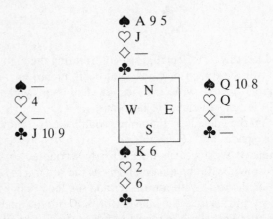

This is in fact what happened, but when Aunt Agatha played her last diamond Mildred threw the four of hearts!

Before Aunt Agatha could discard the knave of hearts from dummy, Issie exploded, 'Why on earth did you have to throw that heart?'

'Well, it was no good to me,' replied Mildred, somewhat taken aback by Issie's outburst, 'and in any case I got bored throwing clubs all the time.'

So Aunt Agatha landed her contract, thanks to Mildred, although the purist may well be forgiven for harbouring doubts about her technique. As for Mildred, she still thinks Issie was a little unreasonable for 'harping on about that silly four of hearts'.

THE LAST SAY

Aunt Agatha took an unnecessary risk in playing on spades at trick three. Of course East was likely to hold the queen, but if he held it originally it would still be there later on. Furthermore, it was improbable that East would have remained silent throughout the bidding if holding *all* the missing hearts—K Q 10 9 to eight—thus it looked as though West must have a heart or two in addition to her nine clubs. The diamond position could be ascertained easily enough, and with that information recorded the final clue to success would surely emerge. In the event West would have shown up with two diamonds: thus all the declarer has to do, having drawn trumps, is to play the two of hearts. The moment West follows (marking her with nine clubs, two diamonds and one heart) the play of the spade suit can hardly present a great problem. If by any chance West shows out of hearts, then East becomes a marked target for a major-suit squeeze. In fact the play of the ace of hearts, instead of the two, which superficially looks wrong because you cannot then rectify the count for a squeeze in the event of West showing out, works just as well because the squeeze operates effectively without the count. This would be the end position:

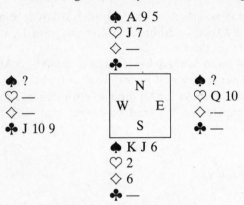

On the six of diamonds, dummy throws the five of spades and declarer awaits East's pleasure. If he throws a spade, then the spades must drop, and if he throws a heart a trick can be established in this suit.

One final word about Mildred's bidding: although the actual sequence would hardly make anyone's hair stand on end outside expert circles, it is not to be recommended. If she thinks her hand is worth a bid of 5 ♣, which is not an unreasonable assessment, then she should bid it immediately and leave the rest to her partner. To bid 4 ♣ and then follow with 5 ♣ is a form of back-seat driving and insulting to partner. It's like informing him that you know more about his thirteen cards than he does himself. Understandably, therefore, such contortions are unlikely to boost the bank balance over the years.

Whatever we may think of Aunt Agatha's technique on the last hand, she certainly gave a flawless exhibition when confronted with the following deal.

Love all

Dealer East

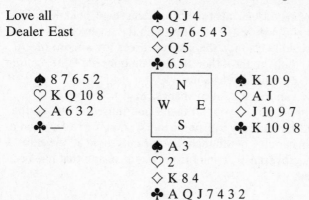

♠ Q J 4
♡ 9 7 6 5 4 3
◇ Q 5
♣ 6 5

♠ 8 7 6 5 2
♡ K Q 10 8
◇ A 6 3 2
♣ —

♠ K 10 9
♡ A J
◇ J 10 9 7
♣ K 10 9 8

♠ A 3
♡ 2
◇ K 8 4
♣ A Q J 7 4 3 2

The bidding:

S	W	N	E
(A. A.)	(Mildred)	(F. N.)	(Issie)
—	—	—	1 NT
Dble	Rdble	2 ♡	No
3 ♣	No	No	Dble
No	No	No	

Mildred was a very hesitant redoubler, with good reason, and even more hesitant about passing her partner's double. Maybe the last hand had upset her judgement a little. Certainly Issie's comments about her discard of the four of hearts had not helped one tiny bit. Be that as it may, Aunt Agatha still needed the gods on her side, and it cannot be denied that every card was working overtime.

Mildred led the king of hearts, which Issie overtook to lead the eight of clubs. When the knave of clubs held, Aunt Agatha played a low diamond to the queen. The queen of spades took the next trick and was followed by a heart ruff, the ace of spades and then the *king* of diamonds. Mildred won and led a spade which Aunt Agatha ruffed. Now a diamond ruffed in dummy and a heart ruffed in hand reduced each player to three cards. Aunt

Agatha, who had lost only two tricks at this stage, held ♣ A Q 7, while Issie held ♣ K 10 9. Exiting with the seven of clubs Aunt Agatha proudly claimed the last two tricks for a score of 270.

'Same result in the other room,' announced Aunt Agatha wickedly and quite irrelevantly.

'But we can make a lot of spades,' said Issie.

'Impossible, unless you bid them,' murmured Aunt Agatha.

As Mildred was busy explaining to Issie that she had wanted to bid over his double but thought that he must hold all the clubs, I was mulling over in my mind the various atrocities that had been committed.

THE LAST SAY

The first bid of doubtful character is surely West's redouble. I suppose the argument goes like this: 'Partner must have between twelve and fourteen points, thus we hold the balance of power. So surely it is only a question of where, and by how much, we clobber them.' Neat and tidy, maybe. But not too realistic, since we may well founder on the rocks of distribution. Furthermore, the balance of power is not so much in our favour that it necessitates an immediate show of teeth. Far better to remain camouflaged for the time being and await developments. As the bidding went, Issie's double of 3 ♣ looks impeccable, but once again West's action savours of walking the tightrope. Call me chicken if you will, but my money would go fairly and squarely on removing the double to 3 ♠. It is funny how often players assume, when they hold a void or singleton in any particular suit, that partner, when he doubles, must be loaded. All too frequently of course it transpires that partner has a perfectly normal minimal holding, while it is dummy that turns up with the missing length.

Finally, Mildred committed her third error during the defence. When she won trick seven with the ace of diamonds this was the position, with her side having taken just two tricks:

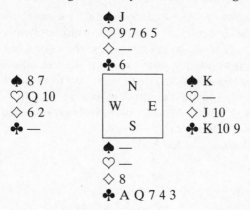

You'll recall that Mildred now played a spade, which enabled Aunt Agatha to reduce her trumps to four. A diamond ruff in dummy and yet a further heart ruff reduced her trumps to three—the same number as East. Since Aunt Agatha was clearly trying to take ruffs in her own hand, and the spade situation was obvious enough, Mildred should have played a diamond. This ploy would have prevented Aunt Agatha reducing her trumps effectively, and although the contract would not have been defeated the ignominy of the overtrick would have been averted.

The very first hand of the next rubber again provided some excitement. Consider my problem as North. Aunt Agatha (South) dealt and bid 1 ♡, Mildred (West) bid 4 ♠, and this was my hand:

♠ —
♡ A J 9
♢ A J 7 6 5
♣ A Q 9 5 2

Immediately, it's not difficult. I bid 5 ♣ with some confidence; but then the pace hotted up. Issie (East) bid 6 ♣, Aunt Agatha doubled and Mildred passed. What should I do now? I toyed with the idea of bidding 6 NT. That would be an unusual sequence, but no doubt the message *should* be decipherable. If decoded accurately it would certainly obviate the difficulty of trying to guess which seven to bid. However, I couldn't help wondering just how Aunt Agatha would react to such a move. Furthermore, there were sure to be distributional storms ahead; maybe the prudent course was to 'take the money'. So, I passed. Would that have been your decision? If so, what would you lead?

Time to look at the full hand:

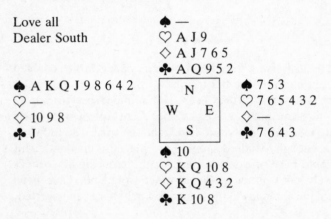

```
Love all            ♠ —
Dealer South        ♡ A J 9
                    ◇ A J 7 6 5
                    ♣ A Q 9 5 2

♠ A K Q J 9 8 6 4 2      N        ♠ 7 5 3
♡ —                              ♡ 7 6 5 4 3 2
◇ 10 9 8         W       E        ◇ —
♣ J                              ♣ 7 6 4 3
                        S
                    ♠ 10
                    ♡ K Q 10 8
                    ◇ K Q 4 3 2
                    ♣ K 10 8
```

This had been our auction:

S	W	N	E
(A. A.)	(Mildred)	(F. N.)	(Issie)
1 ♡	4 ♠	5 ♠	6 ♠
Dble	No	No	No

If you selected a low club for your opening lead, so that partner could play her singleton trump, thereby defeating the contract by one trick, then I suspect you've been cheating! If you led something else, like me, now is the time to polish up your alibi routine, since all hope of defeating the contract has vanished. What North/South can actually make is probably academic as

Mildred would almost certainly have continued to 7 ♠. So much for my 'take the money' policy.

'What a lucky hand for them!' groaned Aunt Agatha with some feeling.

'Lucky nothing,' retorted Issie. 'We outbid you. Besides, you can't expect to make your grand slams if you don't even mention your best suit.' *Touché*.

'Don't forget a hundred honours,' piped in Mildred, who looked quite overcome with the effort of actually making her laydown contract.

THE LAST SAY

If ever a hand illustrated how much more important it is to have shape rather than points, then this must surely be the one. As Issie himself put it on another occasion, 'Not every girl would agree that shape is a better possession than firm collateral, but— properly exploited—the former usually provides the greater bargaining power.' I suspect Issie of having his tongue in his cheek, but his analogy bears the closest inspection.

Without doubt this was a fiendish hand, and if anyone should take the blame it must be me since Aunt Agatha's double was eminently correct. With one loser in the opponent's suit, and an aceless hand to boot, it is normal practice to warn partner against embarking on a grand slam when the opponents appear to be sacrificing. The double does just that. In retrospect, I suppose North should definitely have bid 6 NT over 6 ♠ doubled, even with Aunt Agatha as a partner. After all, the bid of 5 ♠ had set the wheels in motion, and it would need a particularly moronic South to misread the message.

A total of 1010 to Issie and Mildred, when we should have been recording a plus score, was not an auspicious start to the rubber, but Aunt Agatha, perhaps determined to get even after this disaster, pulled off a great coup a few hands later.

This was the deal.

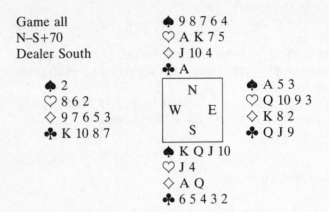

Game all
N–S+70
Dealer South

♠ 9 8 7 6 4
♡ A K 7 5
♢ J 10 4
♣ A

♠ 2
♡ 8 6 2
♢ 9 7 6 5 3
♣ K 10 8 7

N
W   E
S

♠ A 5 3
♡ Q 10 9 3
♢ K 8 2
♣ Q J 9

♠ K Q J 10
♡ J 4
♢ A Q
♣ 6 5 4 3 2

The bidding:

S	W	N	E
(A. A.)	(Mildred)	(F. N.)	(Issie)
1 ♠	No	3 ♡	No
3 NT	No	4 ♠	No
5 ♢	No	6 ♣	No
No	No		

Well, we certainly left nothing unbid, but to be fair the contract looked playable until Mildred, who had been fumbling with one card after another in her inimitable style, hesitantly placed the two of spades on the table. Issie took his ace and returned a spade. After the ace of clubs, a diamond finesse, a club ruff, the ace of diamonds and a second club ruff, Aunt Agatha was in dummy. Now the ace and king of hearts and a heart ruff left the following three-card ending. South to play, having lost just one trick:

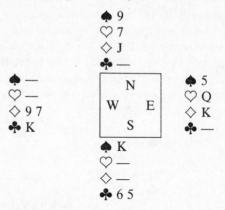

```
              ♠ 9
              ♡ 7
              ◇ J
              ♣ —
♠ —       ┌─────────┐      ♠ 5
♡ —       │    N    │      ♡ Q
◇ 9 7     │ W     E │      ◇ K
♣ K       │    S    │      ♣ —
          └─────────┘
              ♠ K
              ♡ —
              ◇ —
              ♣ 6 5
```

When Aunt Agatha led the five of clubs and ruffed in dummy poor Issie looked most unhappy, as well he might. He couldn't spare any of his three cards without conceding the remainder of the tricks. In fact, he was squeezed in three suits, including trumps.

'Is there any better lead?' asked Mildred, apprehensive lest she had given the contract.

'Not at all,' conceded Issie magnanimously, 'anything else and the hand would have been a spread. As it was Agatha had to play really well to get home. Damned lucky nevertheless.'

Needless to say, Aunt Agatha was absolutely delighted with her success, although perhaps not quite clear how it had all come about. What mattered was that she had made her slam when all seemed lost, and that made up for many of the earlier set-backs.

THE LAST SAY

Aunt Agatha had in fact executed a very rare type of squeeze discovered by the Australian expert Tim Seres, and named the 'Sydney Squeeze', since Tim was playing there at the time. The key factor in the end position is that while pressure is brought to bear in two suits there is a non-winning trump which also needs to be retained, so that it is no solution to underruff.

For the next rubber Sally replaced Mildred and duly cut with Issie, so Aunt Agatha and I were still in partnership—if that is the right way to describe it. The following hand strained the family relationship a bit, but I am fairly confident that more august partnerships than ours would have found some difficulty in steering a clear course. Let us see what you would have done in Aunt Agatha's position as East.

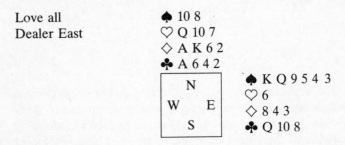

Love all
Dealer East

♠ 10 8
♡ Q 10 7
◇ A K 6 2
♣ A 6 4 2

♠ K Q 9 5 4 3
♡ 6
◇ 8 4 3
♣ Q 10 8

The bidding:

S	W	N	E
(Issie)	(F. N.)	(Sally)	(A. A.)
—	—	—	No
No	No	1 ◇	No
1 ♡	No	2 ♡	No
4 ♡	No	No	No

The lead is the three of clubs. Dummy plays low and your queen wins, declarer contributing the five. What now?

This was the full deal:

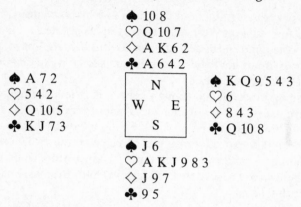

Thinking that it might be necessary to establish some club winners before dummy's diamond suit was set up, I decided on an attacking lead; hence the three of clubs. There was a pregnant pause while Aunt Agatha considered what to do next. Eventually she played the king of spades, and when I followed with the two she switched back to the ten of clubs. But already it was too late. Issie won in dummy, cashed the ace of hearts and then played the knave of spades. I won and continued with the king of clubs but declarer ruffed in hand and then ran off all his hearts. This was the four-card ending:

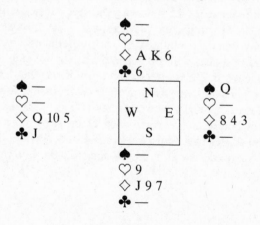

Needing the remainder of the tricks to fulfil his contract, Issie put the pressure on West when he played his last heart. I had to let go a diamond and hope that Aunt Agatha held the knave, but, of course, it was not to be. The ace, king and knave of diamonds took the last three tricks.

'Nothing you could do about it,' chortled Issie, delighted with the turn of events. 'You were always going to be squeezed in the minors, Freddie, as long as you held the queen of diamonds.'

'But suppose Aunt Agatha returns a club at trick two?' I said.

'Nonsense!' interrupted my aunt. 'I knew from your lead that there were no more tricks to take in clubs. Besides, I had to show my spades.'

THE LAST SAY

I don't know why it was that Aunt Agatha never got into the bidding. It was unlike her not to mention her spade suit, and I can only assume that she was thinking of something else at the time. As to the defence, Aunt Agatha would certainly have given us our best chance had she continued clubs at trick two. Now, should Issie decide to play two rounds of spades in order to rectify the count for a squeeze, we just have time to destroy dummy's club menace. Declarer wins the second trick with the ace of clubs, draws trumps and plays a spade. East must win this trick and play her third club. West will subsequently win the second round of spades with his ace and play his last club. With dummy's menace in clubs effectively neutralized, the defence can sit back and wait for the fourth trick in the greatest of comfort. However, eagle-eyed analysts will have noted that declarer does better not to rectify the count fully when East returns a club at trick two. Suppose, as suggested, declarer draws trumps, plays a spade—won by East—and ruffs the club return. This is the position:

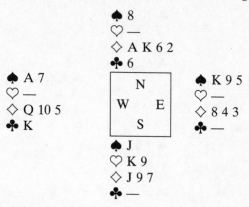

```
                    ♠ 8
                    ♡ —
                    ◇ A K 6 2
                    ♣ 6
♠ A 7          ┌─────────────┐      ♠ K 9 5
♡ —            │      N      │      ♡ —
◇ Q 10 5       │  W       E  │      ◇ 8 4 3
♣ K            │      S      │      ♣ —
               └─────────────┘
                    ♠ J
                    ♡ K 9
                    ◇ J 9 7
                    ♣ —
```

If South now plays his last two hearts West is in trouble, although the normal requirements of losing the requisite number of tricks early on has not been achieved. On the king of hearts West can part with a spade, let's say the ace, but when South's last heart appears all West's cards are busy, either protecting or forming a link. A second spade discard will put off the evil moment, but it won't take declarer long to play a diamond to the ace and then throw West in with the king of clubs to lead away from his queen of diamonds.

An alternative ending, although this time savouring strongly of double dummy analysis, embraces a different technique. Winning the second trick with the ace of clubs, declarer draws trumps and plays the knave of diamonds, forcing West to cover. He then ruffs a club and cashes all his remaining trumps. This will be the position before the last trump is played.

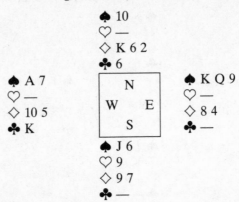

Remember, South has lost only one trick. When he cashes the nine of hearts West has to throw the ace of spades in order to avoid being end-played. Dummy throws a diamond, and now East must throw the nine of spades as she cannot afford to blank the eight of diamonds. East is now thrown in with a spade and has the unenviable choice of cashing a second spade and squeezing her partner or playing a diamond for South to make his extra trick.

The very next hand, apart from being an object-lesson in common sense and a stern reminder of the dangers of allowing the tail to wag the dog, did a great deal to deflate the ebullient Issie. Consider Sally's problem as North. She held:

♠ A 8 5 3
♡ K 7 4
◇ A K 7 2
♣ K 5

This was the bidding:

S	W	N	E
(Issie)	(F. N.)	(Sally)	(A. A.)
1 NT*	No	2 ♣	No
2 ♠	No	?	
* 16–18			

What should Sally bid now and, as a matter of interest, do you approve of her bidding so far? In fact, with hardly a second's thought, Sally's choice was 6 ♠ and everyone passed. This was the full deal:

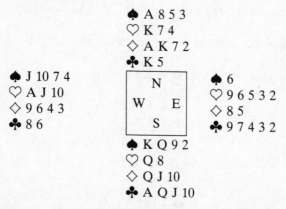

```
                    ♠ A 8 5 3
                    ♡ K 7 4
                    ◇ A K 7 2
                    ♣ K 5
   ♠ J 10 7 4          N          ♠ 6
   ♡ A J 10                       ♡ 9 6 5 3 2
   ◇ 9 6 4 3     W         E      ◇ 8 5
   ♣ 8 6             S           ♣ 9 7 4 3 2
                    ♠ K Q 9 2
                    ♡ Q 8
                    ◇ Q J 10
                    ♣ A Q J 10
```

As you can see, 6 ♠ was not a classic success, since Issie had no way of avoiding the loss of the ace of hearts and a trump trick. When the spades failed to break I really thought Issie was going to tear his hair out—or what little is left of it. Of course, it didn't take long to appreciate that twelve tricks in notrumps would have been a spread.

'Devilishly unlucky,' complained Issie. 'That trump break was all against the odds.'

'Daft bidding, I call it,' interjected Aunt Agatha. 'When you have the values to bid six notrumps direct why go looking for a four-leaf clover?'

Well, what did you make of that bidding sequence? Did you avoid the trap into which Sally fell?

THE LAST SAY

On this occasion I find myself siding with Aunt Agatha. When a pair holds so much overall strength, the dangers of playing in a slightly delicate trump suit far outweigh the possible advantages of the 4-4 fit. Paradoxically, had Sally been weaker in top cards she might well have been right to try for a slam in one of her suits, since a ruffing value could now be essential. As it was, there was some justice when the clover turned out to be a nettle.

After a few insignificant exchanges this deal emerged:

```
N–S game            ♠ A K Q
Dealer North        ♡ K
                    ◇ K 10 8 5 3
                    ♣ K 9 8 4
                    ┌───────────┐
                    │     N     │
                    │  W     E  │
                    │     S     │
                    └───────────┘
                    ♠ J 10 9 7 6 4
                    ♡ A 5
                    ◇ J
                    ♣ A 10 7 3
```

This was the bidding:

S	W	N	E
(Sally)	(F. N.)	(Issie)	(A. A.)
—	—	1 ◇	No
1 ♠	No	3 ♣	No
4 ♣	No	4 ♠	No
4 NT	No	5 ◇	No
6 ♠	No	No	No

Maybe this is not the greatest bidding sequence you ever encountered, but give them some credit for avoiding 6 ♣, a vastly inferior contract to 6 ♠. How should Sally plan the play against West's opening lead of the two of hearts?

Sally won in dummy with the king of hearts and led a low diamond. West took this trick with the queen and led a second heart. After some thought Sally ruffed in dummy and then attempted to crash the ace of diamonds in two more rounds. When this failed she had to try and bring in the club suit without loss—another impossible task. This was the full deal:

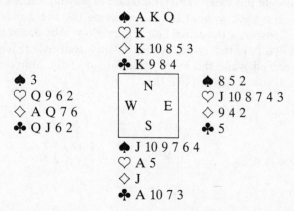

Aunt Agatha and I were a shade lucky to score here since Sally was obviously blinded by that obscurantist king of hearts. Had the king of hearts been a small card no doubt she would have made her contract, for then she would have been in her own hand at trick one. Now the lead of the knave of diamonds towards dummy would have left West powerless. By setting up the diamond suit declarer makes six spades, one heart, one heart ruff, two clubs and two diamonds.

Issie was inclined to be critical of Sally's play for quite the wrong reason. He suggested that she should have come to hand with the ace of clubs in order to lead a diamond, but as Aunt Agatha pointed out: 'No doubt even my partner would have been sufficiently wide awake to have given me a club ruff—so clearly marked on the bidding.' Charming! The real point of this hand, overtaking the king of hearts with the ace at trick one, seemed to be missed by Sally and her partner, and perhaps by Aunt Agatha as well, since she is not exactly renowned for her reticence.

THE LAST SAY

At first sight this looks like a typical case of playing automatically to the first trick without fully considering the two hands as a whole. However, the actual line of play adopted by declarer was not all that bad. Indeed, there are certain layouts where it might well succeed while the more orthodox line fails. Suppose the diamond suit is divided like this:

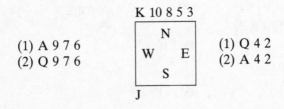

K 10 8 5 3

(1) A 9 7 6
(2) Q 9 7 6

(1) Q 4 2
(2) A 4 2

J

Now the normal method of coming to hand and leading the knave of diamonds might fail if West keeps his cool and declarer makes the wrong guess. But small to the knave will certainly succeed in the second case, no matter which card East plays, and also in the first unless East hops up with the queen. As it happens the play of the queen is perhaps more obvious than it might seem since South is marked with two hearts (West led the two), four clubs and almost certainly a six-card spade suit in view of her aggressive bidding when lacking the A K Q of trumps. On this basis there is only room for one diamond, so inserting the queen cannot cost.

Still, having given Sally's line of play more marks than Issie was prepared to concede, I have no doubt that the combined mathematical and psychological advantages lie with leading the knave of diamonds towards dummy.

Aunt Agatha found a smart defence on the next hand, when once again we were silenced by the opposition's big guns.

♠ K 10 5 4 2
♡ J 8 6
♢ A 9 5
♣ A 4

♠ 3
♡ K 9 7 4
♢ Q 7 4
♣ K 9 8 7 6

This was the bidding:

S	W	N	E
(Sally)	(F. N.)	(Issie)	(A. A.)
—	—	1 NT*	No
3 ♠	No	4 ♣	No
4 ♡	No	5 ♢	No
6 ♠	No	No	No
* *12–14*			

West led the ten of clubs, and dummy played low. How should East plan the defence?

This was the full hand:

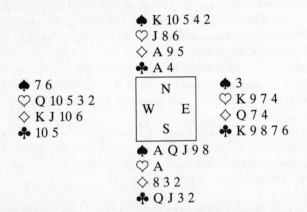

♠ K 10 5 4 2
♥ J 8 6
♢ A 9 5
♣ A 4

♠ 7 6
♥ Q 10 5 3 2
♢ K J 10 6
♣ 10 5

♠ 3
♥ K 9 7 4
♢ Q 7 4
♣ K 9 8 7 6

♠ A Q J 9 8
♥ A
♢ 8 3 2
♣ Q J 3 2

Aunt Agatha decided that South just had to have ♣ Q J x x, in which case she might gain more by ducking than contributing her king immediately. Of course she lost this trick and we never came to a club trick at all, but we gained two diamond tricks in compensation.

'Two for one is never a bad dividend, you know, Freddie,' crowed Aunt Agatha, as the full implication of her thoughtful play to the first trick became apparent.

'That was brilliant, Aunt Agatha,' I murmured encouragingly, 'but of course only to be expected.' Aunt Agatha shot a suspicious glance in my direction, but my nose was buried in a glass of vodka and tonic.

THE LAST SAY

Issie and Sally stretched a bit in getting to 6 ♠. It's one thing to have all the controls, but it is not enough if there are insufficient tricks. However, once I had failed to find a diamond lead South had some hopes. Left to her own devices she must forgo the club finesse, for that will not help her should West hold the king. Instead, she must play the ace and a low club, or perhaps a low club away from the ace. Now if East goes wrong the slam will succeed. As the play went, Aunt Agatha's most telling card is the nine of clubs, since it precludes the possibility of my having led from the top of an interior sequence (Q 10 9, etc.). Once East has realized that South must hold something like ♣ Q J x x (West wouldn't lead the ten from 10 x x) it can only be right to contribute the king if East suspects the lead to be a singleton, or if a second trick is certain.

'It's our turn to hold the goodies now,' remarked Aunt Agatha, as East dealt the next hand of interest.

E–W game
Dealer East

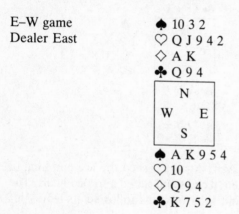

♠ 10 3 2
♡ Q J 9 4 2
◇ A K
♣ Q 9 4

N
W   E
S

♠ A K 9 5 4
♡ 10
◇ Q 9 4
♣ K 7 5 2

The bidding:

S (A. A.)	W (Sally)	N (F. N.)	E (Issie)
—	—	—	No
1 ♠	No	2 ♡	No
2 ♣	No	4 ♠	No
No	No		

West led the knave of clubs, which East won with the ace. East now cashed the king of hearts and, despite West's three, continued with the ace. Aunt Agatha ruffed in hand and then stopped for a moment to consider Issie's odd defence. Not making much sense of it, she cashed the ace of spades, West following with the seven and East with the six. What now?

As Aunt Agatha was pondering on her next move a voice on her left said, 'Don't worry, my dear, this is one contract you are not going to make.' A provocative remark to address to such a versatile character as my aunt! This was the full hand:

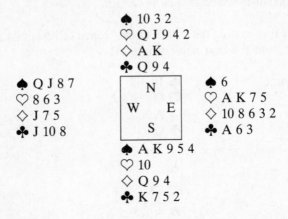

                    ♠ 10 3 2
                    ♡ Q J 9 4 2
                    ◇ A K
                    ♣ Q 9 4
    ♠ Q J 8 7   N   ♠ 6
    ♡ 8 6 3   ♡ A K 7 5
    ◇ J 7 5   W   E   ◇ 10 8 6 3 2
    ♣ J 10 8   S   ♣ A 6 3
                    ♠ A K 9 5 4
                    ♡ 10
                    ◇ Q 9 4
                    ♣ K 7 5 2

Without more ado Aunt Agatha cashed the ace and king of diamonds and the queen of clubs and ruffed a second heart. The queen of diamonds and king of clubs followed to leave this position—South to play:

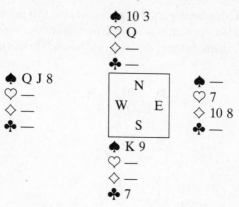

♠ 10 3
♡ Q
♢ —
♣ —

♠ Q J 8   ♠ —
♡ —   ♡ 7
♢ —   ♢ 10 8
♣ —   ♣ —

♠ K 9
♡ —
♢ —
♣ 7

When the seven of clubs appeared on the table West wriggled uncomfortably, Aunt Agatha smiled sweetly and East looked daggers at his partner. 'Now, what was it you were saying, Sally dear?' enquired Aunt Agatha, still smiling as she poured salt into the wound.

THE LAST SAY

There is no doubt that Sally's thoughtless remark was quite inexcusable. But many players who have not the ability, or the foresight, to visualize the possibilities open to a resourceful player are guilty of just such lapses. Perhaps Issie was rather naive in trying to cash two heart tricks—Sally would surely have petered with a doubleton—since this seemed to indicate that he expected to find a spade trick, or tricks, in his partner's hand. As the play went perhaps Aunt Agatha would have succeeded even without Sally's untimely outburst. Suppose the defence is a little more subtle (ducking the first club would present declarer with most problems) and Sally manages to zip the lip, there is a great deal to be said for continuing along general crossruff lines. Although a true count may never be obtained, an inferential count may be sufficient to steer the contract home.

There had certainly been plenty of excitement in this rubber, but the final hand was perhaps the *pièce de résistance*, with Aunt Agatha once again taking the star role—and performing it brilliantly.

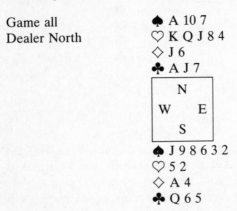

Game all
Dealer North

♠ A 10 7
♡ K Q J 8 4
◇ J 6
♣ A J 7

♠ J 9 8 6 3 2
♡ 5 2
◇ A 4
♣ Q 6 5

The bidding:

S	W	N	E
(A. A.)	(Sally)	(F. N.)	(Issie)
—	—	1 ♡	No
1 ♠	No	2 ♣	No
2 ♠	No	3 ♠	No
4 ♠	No	No	Dble
No	No	No	

Not, perhaps, the most profound bidding sequence of modern times, but the final contract only started to look really ugly when Issie doubled.

For reasons best known to herself Sally led the four of spades. Aunt Agatha took stock, and it was clear that she didn't much like what she saw. Another good bet was that if the contract failed it would be my fault. Anyway she won the first trick with the ace of spades and played the king of hearts. East won, West discarding the two of clubs, cashed the king and queen of spades,

West discarding the eight and two of diamonds, and switched to the five of diamonds. How should declarer continue?

It is not difficult to appreciate that South's chief concern, having been favoured with a not altogether hostile lead, centres around the club suit. There is a parking place for the losing diamond, but it appears that there must be a club loser, even if the finesse is right. But wait! Going back over the established facts Aunt Agatha realized that the club finesse would serve little purpose, since even if the knave held she could not possibly hope to bring down West's king on the next round. West must have far too many clubs for that to happen. Therefore the only chance of enjoying the club suit without loss, assuming East held the king, was to play him for the bare honour. East was marked with three spades, six hearts and either three or four diamonds, so it was not such a remote shot as one might think. Furthermore, since no other line could succeed, except for a squeeze against West in the minors ($\diamondsuit$ K Q and $\clubsuit$ K) which was unlikely on the bidding, why not try the only one that was plausible?

This was the full deal:

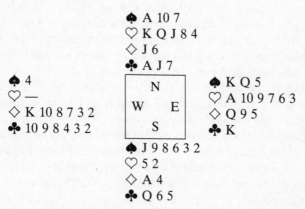

	$\spadesuit$ A 10 7	
	$\heartsuit$ K Q J 8 4	
	$\diamondsuit$ J 6	
	$\clubsuit$ A J 7	

$\spadesuit$ 4
$\heartsuit$ —
$\diamondsuit$ K 10 8 7 3 2
$\clubsuit$ 10 9 8 4 3 2

$\spadesuit$ K Q 5
$\heartsuit$ A 10 9 7 6 3
$\diamondsuit$ Q 9 5
$\clubsuit$ K

$\spadesuit$ J 9 8 6 3 2
$\heartsuit$ 5 2
$\diamondsuit$ A 4
$\clubsuit$ Q 6 5

Aunt Agatha wasted no more time. She won the diamond switch with her ace, cashed two top hearts, ditching her losing diamond, ruffed a diamond in hand and played a club to dummy's ace.

Poor Issie! He looked as though he had just received his final income-tax demand, as the full significance of Aunt Agatha's play struck him. Later, when the dust of battle had all but settled, he gallantly conceded that Aunt Agatha had played a great game—even if his partner had been on her side. And the heroine of the piece? She absorbed it all happily, practically purring with delight.

THE LAST SAY

We shall never know what would have happened without that ill-conceived trump lead, but it is heavy odds-on that the rubber would have continued. Even if the thought of leading a diamond sent cold shivers down West's spine, what possible objection could there be to a club? While a diamond lead would sink declarer without trace, a club attack would do no more than offer a temporary stay of execution—assuming that South does not make two inspired guesses and East does not mistime the defence. Indeed, the most likely outcome after a club lead is defeat by two tricks. In order to succeed declarer will have to go up with the ace of clubs immediately—at this point in the game that play would be all against the odds—take one round of spades only (the ace) and then lead a top heart. If East makes the mistake of accepting this trick, or ducking the first round, winning the second and then cashing both his spade winners, declarer will succeed. Somebody else, certainly not I, can compute the probable odds of that happening—if he considers such an exercise fruitful. Despite the luck of the lead, full marks to Aunt Agatha for finding a line of play that offered a small chance of success. The moral is simple: prefer the improbable to the impossible!

Aunt Agatha was so pleased at the outcome of the last rubber that she insisted on playing with me again, Mildred replacing Sally as Issie's partner. It wasn't long, however, before she eyed

her favourite nephew with considerable disapproval. This was
the hand that incurred her displeasure.

Love all

Dealer South

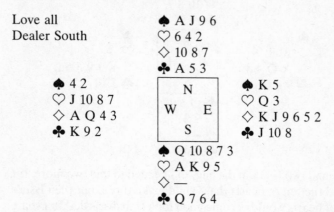

```
                        ♠ A J 9 6
                        ♡ 6 4 2
                        ◇ 10 8 7
                        ♣ A 5 3
    ♠ 4 2              ┌─────────┐      ♠ K 5
    ♡ J 10 8 7         │    N    │      ♡ Q 3
    ◇ A Q 4 3          │ W     E │      ◇ K J 9 6 5 2
    ♣ K 9 2            │    S    │      ♣ J 10 8
                        └─────────┘
                        ♠ Q 10 8 7 3
                        ♡ A K 9 5
                        ◇ —
                        ♣ Q 7 6 4
```

The bidding:

S	W	N	E
(Issie)	(F. N.)	(Mildred)	(A. A.)
1 ♠	No	2 ♠	No
3 ♣	No	4 ♠	No
No	No		

As you'll observe, they didn't forget to bid a thing. Issie's game
try was imaginative, but Mildred could hardly do less than accept
it with 4 ♠ once Issie had taken the plunge.

I led the knave of hearts and Aunt Agatha unblocked the
queen—not that it matters what she does. Issie won, took a
losing spade finesse and won the heart continuation in his hand.
A spade to the ace and a low club to the queen and king left me on
lead with the remaining cards distributed as follows:

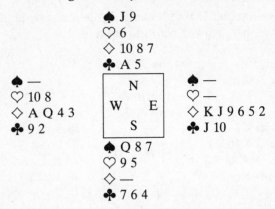

We had two tricks in the bag, so I needed to find two more. If I cashed the ten of hearts that would make three, but then Issie's nine of hearts would become good for a club discard. After some thought I played a club, which Aunt Agatha was allowed to win. Subsequently declarer discarded his losing heart from dummy on the thirteenth club.

'Why didn't you cash your heart winner?' demanded Aunt Agatha, speaking without thinking as players are prone to do. Once I had convinced her that this would not have altered the result, only the ending, she switched her attack to firmer ground. 'Anyway, that was a dotty lead. If you start off with a small heart Issie can't possibly make his contract.'

Before I could get in a suitable reply, Issie, who was positively cock-a-hoop with his own efforts in both the bidding and the play, had taken the floor. 'How's that then—making a game try on only eleven points and then steering the contract home via a neat little end-play?' Mildred made encouraging noises, looking very impressed, but Aunt Agatha was not amused.

'You made a gambling bid, and because my partner made an idiotic lead you luckily scrambled home. That's nothing to crow about. You were fortunate that I wasn't on lead, otherwise you would probably have been doubled.'

THE LAST SAY

Despite being rather a bore over this hand, I award Issie my personal accolade for enterprise. Mildred did not have to be so good in terms of high-card points for her raise to 2 ♠, but she might have been more shapely. Indeed, there are many modest shapely hands that North might hold, without diamond pictures, which would give a reasonable play for game, so his trial bid was not all that speculative. The unfortunate aspect of the hand is that if I lead a small heart the contract will almost certainly fail, as indeed it will if I lead a diamond or a spade. However, the book lead is the knave of hearts, and I am sure I will do the same thing next time—despite Aunt Agatha's verbal lash. Just for the record, declarer can always make his contract double-dummy against any lead. Suppose a small heart is led. Declarer wins and plays the queen of clubs, ducking to West. The heart continuation is won in hand and a second club played towards dummy. If West puts in the nine, dummy wins and exits with a club. If West plays small, so does North. Having subsequently negotiated the trumps, declarer has the last club available to dispose of dummy's third heart. Still, as I said, that is really double-dummy stuff and would no doubt require some explanation if employed at the table—especially Aunt Agatha's table.

Now that he had the bit well and truly between his teeth there was no stopping Issie, and the next hand was typical of his ever-glowing optimism. As Aunt Agatha put it: 'The bidding warranted either the George Cross or a one-way ticket to the nearest lunatic asylum.'

N–S game
Dealer West

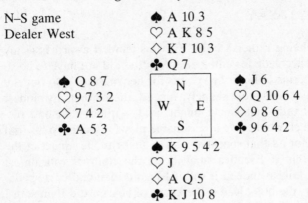

♠ A 10 3
♥ A K 8 5
♦ K J 10 3
♣ Q 7

♠ Q 8 7   ♠ J 6
♥ 9 7 3 2   ♥ Q 10 6 4
♦ 7 4 2   ♦ 9 8 6
♣ A 5 3   ♣ 9 6 4 2

♠ K 9 5 4 2
♥ J
♦ A Q 5
♣ K J 10 8

The bidding:

S	W	N	E
(Issie)	(F. N.)	(Mildred)	(A. A.)
—	No	1 NT	No
3 ♠	No	4 ♠	No
4 NT	No	5 ♥	No
6 ♠	No	No	No

Feeling that I might eventually make my queen of spades, I led
the ace and another club. Issie, who was obviously a little
perturbed at the sight of dummy, took quite a time before
playing to trick three. Then, with a deep sigh, he cashed the ace
of hearts, ruffed a heart and via the two diamond entries ruffed
the last two hearts, which of course included the king. He then
cashed the ace of diamonds and king of clubs to arrive at the
following position. South to play, having lost just one trick:

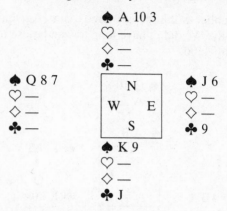

Issie now played the knave of clubs ... and, alas, there was nothing we could do. I did my best by ruffing with the queen of spades, but Issie overruffed and then finessed against Aunt Agatha's knave on the return journey.

'Thank you, Mildred. I enjoyed that rubber,' said Issie, almost before the grisly details of the score had been agreed.

THE LAST SAY

It is hard to argue with success, but the fact remains that Issie was really pushing his luck when he bid 6 ♠. At best the slam could hardly be better than on a finesse, and it's worth remembering that Mildred had more encouraging bids than 4 ♠ available to her: 4 ♡, 4 ♢ or 4 ♣ would all agree spades, show a control and generally indicate a willingness to proceed towards slam should that idea grab South in the right place. The more sedate offering of 4 ♠, even allowing for Mildred's natural conservatism, should have warned Issie against setting his sights too high. As it was, he brought off the rare 'Devil's Coup', and I'm sure it never entered his head for a moment that he might have pushed out the boat.

In the next rubber Mildred partnered Aunt Agatha while I played with Sally. We didn't have long to wait before there was another exciting hand.

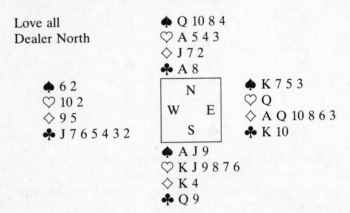

Love all
Dealer North

	♠ Q 10 8 4	
	♡ A 5 4 3	
	◇ J 7 2	
	♣ A 8	

♠ 6 2		♠ K 7 5 3
♡ 10 2		♡ Q
◇ 9 5		◇ A Q 10 8 6 3
♣ J 7 6 5 4 3 2		♣ K 10

	♠ A J 9	
	♡ K J 9 8 7 6	
	◇ K 4	
	♣ Q 9	

The bidding:

S	W	N	E
(A. A.)	(F. N.)	Mildred)	(Sally)
—	—	No	1 ◇
2 ♡	No	4 ♣	No
4 ♠	No	5 ♡	No
6 ♡	No	No	No

After her original pass, Mildred's bid of 4 ♣ clearly showed an interest in hearts, a maximum point-count and the ace of clubs, which was quite sufficient to get Aunt Agatha's adrenalin going.

Without my crystal ball to consult, I dutifully led my partner's suit—the nine of diamonds. However, Aunt Agatha soon showed me the error of my ways. Sally took her ace of diamonds and returned the suit. A trump to the ace was followed by the ten of spades, which held, and then a spade to the knave. The last trump was drawn, the ace of spades cashed and then the trumps run to arrive at the following position, South to play:

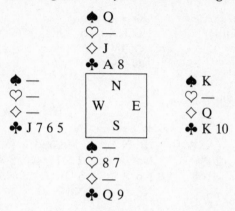

♠ Q
♡ —
◇ J
♣ A 8

♠ —   ♠ K
♡ —   ♡ —
◇ —   ◇ Q
♣ J 7 6 5   ♣ K 10

♠ —
♡ 8 7
◇ —
♣ Q 9

When the eight of hearts was led dummy parted with the eight of clubs, and East was caught in a three-suit criss-cross squeeze. In fact Sally took her best chance by throwing the ten of clubs but Aunt Agatha merely gave her a pitying look as she cashed the ace of clubs and claimed the rest.

THE LAST SAY

Perhaps Sally should have had more foresight. Mildred's jump to 4 ♣ indicated a control, probably the ace, but not necessarily length (3 ♣ would have been forcing and shown a suit), so it was reasonably certain that West would be on lead. In that case a double over 4 ♣ would have alerted West to the necessity of leading a club and saved Sally from that fateful end position when she suffered from a severe *embarras de richesse*.

I wonder if you would have improved on my display as West when this hand occurred just two deals later.

N–S game   ♠ 9 4
Dealer South   ♡ K 10 8 5 3 2
                ♢ 3
                ♣ 9 8 6 4

The bidding:

S	W	N	E
(A. A.)	(F. N.)	(Mildred)	(Sally)
2 ♣	No	2 NT	3 ♠
4 NT	No	5 ♡	No
7 ♢	No	No	No

Well, which card would you lead? Lacking inspiration, I again
made the pedestrian choice of my partner's suit—crazy fool that I
am. The last hand should have warned me that it was not a good
day for partner's suit, although on this occasion it was not so
much the suit that mattered—it was the card. You do lead the top
card from a doubleton, don't you? I thought so, too. With the
nine of spades on the table, then, it's time to look at the full hand.

         ♠ A Q 2
         ♡ Q 7 6 4
         ♢ J 9 2
         ♣ A 5 3

♠ 9 4	**N**	♠ K J 10 7 6 5
♡ K 10 8 5 3 2	**W** **E**	♡ J 9
♢ 3		♢ 5
♣ 9 8 6 4	**S**	♣ Q J 10 7

         ♠ 8 3
         ♡ A
         ♢ A K Q 10 8 7 6 4
         ♣ K 2

With twelve tricks accounted for, Aunt Agatha proceeded to
the grand slam on the general basis that if there are twelve on top

then one more will surely emerge from somewhere. 'Besides,' she explained in her most charming manner when the hand was all over, 'with Freddie on lead I was entitled to expect a little help.'

Aunt Agatha won the first trick with the ace of spades, cashed the red-suit aces and then entered dummy twice with diamonds in an effort to ruff out the king of hearts. When this proved an abortive exercise she ran all her diamonds to arrive at the following position, South to play:

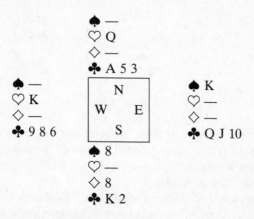

When the eight of diamonds was played we were caught in a double squeeze. I had to part with a club in order to retain heart control, so dummy let go the queen of hearts since she had served her purpose. East had to retain the king of spades so she also parted with a club. Dummy's five of clubs took the thirteenth trick.

THE LAST SAY

It was cute of Aunt Agatha to have noticed just how I had helped her on her way. Her powers of analysis are sometimes sharper than I imagine. It all happened with that wretched nine of spades. Suppose I had led the four of spades—or any other small card for that matter—then this would have been the end position:

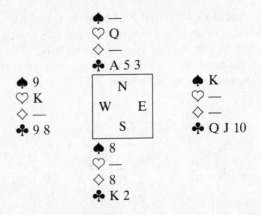

This time, quite correctly, West has already parted with two clubs. Now when South plays the eight of diamonds West can safely throw another club. East is also off the hook, since she can throw the king of spades.

The principle of leading a small trump from some such holding as 8 6 2, or even 8 2, is well known. Perhaps there should be a further extension when defending against a grand slam: avoid parting with any high card if a lower one will do as well.

For the next rubber I enjoyed the role of kibitzer, which was something of a relief after the last few hands. Aunt Agatha by now was in a really buoyant mood. I am sure that without much effort she could have managed to purr. Her partner was Sally and the opposition Mildred and Issie. This was the first deal:

Love all
Dealer West

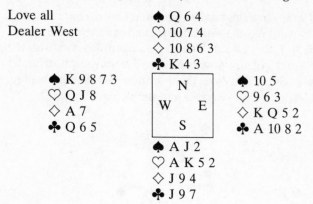

♠ Q 6 4
♡ 10 7 4
◇ 10 8 6 3
♣ K 4 3

♠ K 9 8 7 3
♡ Q J 8
◇ A 7
♣ Q 6 5

♠ 10 5
♡ 9 6 3
◇ K Q 5 2
♣ A 10 8 2

♠ A J 2
♡ A K 5 2
◇ J 9 4
♣ J 9 7

The bidding:

S (A. A.)	W (Mildred)	N (Sally)	E (Issie)
—	No	No	No
1 NT	Dble	No	No
No			

Whether the nervous and hesitant Mildred had miscounted her points or simply didn't fancy opening on her miserable collection of tram tickets was something that was never made clear. However, on the second round Mildred was certainly braver, or perhaps more foolhardy, than most players would have been. The others, for their own various reasons, decided to leave well alone and let Aunt Agatha get on with it.

Mildred led the seven of spades, and, as you'll observe, Aunt Agatha has quite a task on her hands. One or two down seems inevitable, but making assumptions in Aunt Agatha's case is an unprofitable pastime. She won the first trick in dummy with the queen of spades and led a low diamond. Issie would have done well to go in with the queen and play a spade, but he ducked and Mildred took the knave with her ace. Deciding that the spade continuation was too dangerous, Mildred switched to the queen of hearts and, when this card was allowed to win, continued with the knave. Aunt Agatha won this trick and exited with the nine of diamonds to East's queen. The spade return was won with the ace, and Aunt Agatha now cashed two hearts, each defender throwing a club. This was the position with South to play, declarer having won five tricks and the defence three:

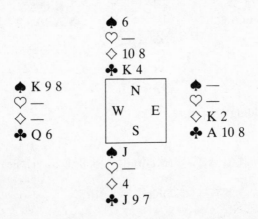

        ♠ 6
        ♡ —
        ♢ 10 8
        ♣ K 4

♠ K 9 8   ♠ —
♡ —   ♡ —
♢ —   ♢ K 2
♣ Q 6   ♣ A 10 8

        ♠ J
        ♡ —
        ♢ 4
        ♣ J 9 7

Seldom have I seen a bridge-player struggling so hard not to gloat over the unconditional surrender that is only just around the corner. In fact it is slightly out of character for Aunt Agatha to bother to conceal her feelings in any way. But remember, everything had fallen into her lap for a number of hands and consequently she was in the best of moods. Furthermore, the current hand was now like an open book and she was enjoying every moment of it. West's original pass made it certain that she could not hold either the king of diamonds or the ace of clubs. So both opponents were about to be end-played in turn. On the four of diamonds West parted with the eight of spades; East won and exited with his last diamond. Aunt Agatha discarded the knave of spades and Mildred, after some thought, parted with the nine of spades. Had she thrown the six of clubs, Aunt Agatha would have played the king of clubs next and made an overtrick. As it was, the six of spades threw Mildred on lead and forced her to play a club. She did her best by playing a low one, but Aunt Agatha immediately played dummy's four, giving Issie a pitying look as she tabled her cards.

'Unbelievably lucky,' exploded Issie, who had not enjoyed the hand at all.

'Nonsense, Issie,' retorted Aunt Agatha. 'One makes one's own luck. Now, if you had cashed your queen of diamonds before exiting with the ten of spades, think how lucky you would have been.'

THE LAST SAY

Aunt Agatha should have been defeated, but that in no way absolves Mildred for making a fatuous bid. Whether Mildred had really miscounted her points we shall never know. What is certain, however, is that it is no kind of solution to double the second time around. There is a place for this double, but Mildred's hand does not fall into that category. A sensible systematic meaning for doubling a notrump bid after passing is to show a distributional hand with the majors. Something like: ♠ K 9 8 7 3, ♡ Q J 9 8 7, ♢ K 7, ♣ 5. Aunt Agatha was on sound ground when she chided Issie about his defence: he had two chances to play his diamond suit to better advantage and so get Mildred off the hook.

A casual observer might say that Aunt Agatha had a real slice of luck on the next hand when she elected to play in diamonds rather than notrumps. In fact Aunt Agatha claimed two slices of luck, the second being that she and not her partner was playing the hand. This was the deal.

Love all
Dealer West

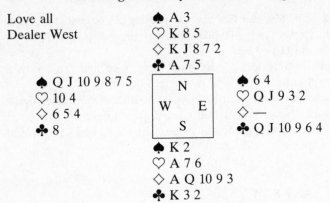

♠ A 3
♡ K 8 5
◇ K J 8 7 2
♣ A 7 5

♠ Q J 10 9 8 7 5
♡ 10 4
◇ 6 5 4
♣ 8

♠ 6 4
♡ Q J 9 3 2
◇ —
♣ Q J 10 9 6 4

♠ K 2
♡ A 7 6
◇ A Q 10 9 3
♣ K 3 2

The bidding:

S	W	N	E
(A. A.)	(Mildred)	(Sally)	(Issie)
—	3 ♠	Dble	No
6 ◇	No	No	No

Aunt Agatha was tempted to bid 6NT but some sixth sense warned her against it.

Mildred led the queen of spades, and at first sight Aunt Agatha was inclined to bemoan her ill-fortune. Eleven tricks on top but apparently no possible way of making twelve—in notrumps or diamonds. No doubt Issie had length in hearts and clubs, but how on earth was declarer to lose a trick in order to bring pressure on him? If Aunt Agatha ducked either a heart or a club she would destroy a vital menace card and with it all chance of a squeeze. Five diamonds and two spades would reduce the hand to six cards, but that wouldn't embarrass East, who would have no difficulty in controlling both vital suits. Aunt Agatha went into one of her rare trances, but the only thing that struck her almost immediately was that Issie was looking extremely smug. No, it was not her imagination. She was sure he was having 'a concealed gloat', as she called it.

Then the penny dropped! If her guardian angel was looking
after her there was a real chance that she could make Mildred
squeeze Issie. What a wonderful spectacle that would be!
Anyway, the plan was formed. Trick two went to the ace of
diamonds, dummy following with the seven, and Aunt Agatha's
heart missed a beat as Issie flamboyantly discarded the queen of
clubs. So far so good. The nine of diamonds was led to the knave,
East throwing the four of clubs. Now the ace of spades, ace of
clubs and the two top hearts set the scene for the kill. The two of
diamonds from dummy and the three from the closed hand
presented an overjoyed Mildred with one of the cheapest tricks
she has ever won.

Mildred's expression turned from joy to pity, and then to
suspicion. As Issie put it later on when he had recovered from his
series of set-backs, 'Mildred had mixed feelings—like the chap
who sees his mother-in-law drive off the cliff in his new car.'
Anyway, back to Mildred, who was wondering what on earth had
come over Aunt Agatha. Concluding that she was either going
round the bend or had had one too many, Mildred suddenly
realized it was her lead. Having no choice in the matter she
played a spade, thus returning the trick that Aunt Agatha had
just given away. Discarding a club from the dummy and ruffing in
her hand, Aunt Agatha had reached this position with South to
play:

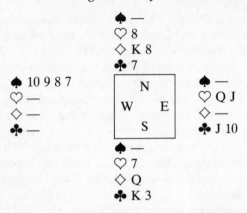

The queen of diamonds was led to dummy's king, Issie throwing a heart but when the eight of diamonds followed Issie had to shut up shop.

'If you don't pull the wrong card and give away that trump trick, I suppose you make seven,' said Sally thoughtlessly.

For once Aunt Agatha replied with considerable restraint, 'No, dear, I go one down. Fortunately, however, our diamonds were bad enough and I was good enough to prevent such a catastrophe.'

THE LAST SAY

One can only admire Aunt Agatha's technique in finding a solution to a nearly insoluble problem. The key to this sort of situation is that you get back what you give away—with the additional bonus of retaining your threat cards. It often happens when a player is playing well that he is lucky, too. There is, of course, a difference, but the two characteristics seem to complement each other.

Although our friends often see us in a rather different light from that which we so fondly imagine portrays our own image, I have never thought of envy as one of my main faults. Yet there are times when I am deeply resentful that I have not the ability to sketch the various moods and quirks of Aunt Agatha at the bridge table: I can see her now, trying hard not to look smug, and making a damned poor job of it. After her recent successes she is positively glowing and although some might have doubts about her smugness, Hollywood can surely relax—she'll never win an Oscar.

This was the next hand of interest.

Love all
N–S+60
Dealer North

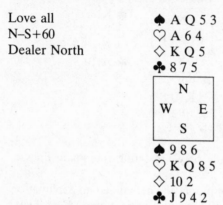

♠ A Q 5 3
♡ A 6 4
♢ K Q 5
♣ 8 7 5

♠ 9 8 6
♡ K Q 8 5
♢ 10 2
♣ J 9 4 2

The bidding:

S	W	N	E
(A. A.)	(Mildred)	(Sally)	(Issie)
—	—	1 NT	2 ◇
2 ♡	No	No	No

West led the four of diamonds. I wonder how you would rate your chances. East took dummy's queen with his ace and switched to a low club. West won with the queen and returned the three of diamonds. Dummy won and played a second club to East's ace. East played the knave of diamonds, South and West discarding spades, and then continued with the ten of clubs to West's king. The defence have five tricks, and West leads the knave of spades. How should South proceed?

After pondering over this problem for only a moment, Aunt Agatha hopped up with the ace of spades dropping East's bare king. Then, when the trumps broke 3–3, she was home and dry. This was the full deal:

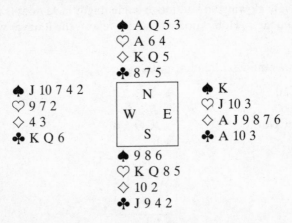

♠ A Q 5 3
♡ A 6 4
◇ K Q 5
♣ 8 7 5

♠ J 10 7 4 2
♡ 9 7 2
◇ 4 3
♣ K Q 6

♠ K
♡ J 10 3
◇ A J 9 8 7 6
♣ A 10 3

♠ 9 8 6
♡ K Q 8 5
◇ 10 2
♣ J 9 4 2

'That was a remarkable play—rejecting the spade finesse,' said Issie accusingly.

Although his comment practically demanded an explanation, Aunt Agatha was obviously not going to be drawn. 'Can't beat a woman's intuition you know, Issie dear,' she purred. In fact Aunt Agatha had made a very shrewd assessment of the position and had the courage to back her judgement in the play. To succeed she needed the trumps to break 3–3. As Issie was marked with six diamonds and three clubs he could only hold one spade—if the trumps were to divide favourably. The question then arose: who had the king of spades. If West had it she would have started life with ♠ K J x x x or even K J 10 x x, plus the king, queen and another club, and with that holding even Mildred would surely have chanced a bid over two hearts—especially in view of the part-score. The obvious conclusion was that West did not hold the king of spades and therefore it had to be singleton with East. A brilliant piece of assumption and analysis by Aunt Agatha.

Although it might have cleared the air a little if she had explained her thought processes to the others, Aunt Agatha seemed to enjoy the role of *mystique extraordinaire*. 'Did you notice, Freddie,' enquired my aunt in a whispered aside to me later on, 'how both Mildred and Issie clasped their cards close to their chests for the remainder of the rubber?' She grinned wickedly and added: 'I think I shall name that coup "Initiating the Bosom Hold".'

THE LAST SAY

There is not much to add. Aunt Agatha's bidding must be questionable, but that is nothing new. She was lucky and played well. That, too, is not without precedent. Whether East makes 2 $\diamondsuit$ will depend on the view declarer takes in trumps. Without any adverse bidding the odds favour a small diamond to the nine. After 1NT by North ... East may get it right.

The next hand saw Aunt Agatha taking full advantage of a helpful defence. The altered positions (Issie and Mildred changed places) were allowed by the opponents because Issie complained that he was too hot beside the fire. Aunt Agatha is always willing to ensure her opponents have no excuses for failure.

N–S game
Dealer South

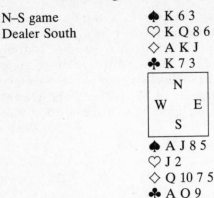

♠ K 6 3
♡ K Q 8 6
◇ A K J
♣ K 7 3

♠ A J 8 5
♡ J 2
◇ Q 10 7 5
♣ A Q 9

The bidding:

S	W	N	E
(A. A.)	(Issie)	(Sally)	(Mildred)
1 NT*	No	2 ♣	No
2 ♠	No	4 NT	No
5 ♡	No	6 NT	No
No	No		
* 12–14			

After Aunt Agatha's weak notrump opening, Sally knew they were on the brink of a slam. Stayman elicited the fact that there was no 4–4 fit, and 4 NT was intended as a quantitative bid, saying in effect: 'Go to six if you are maximum.' Aunt Agatha was not sure how Sally meant this last bid, but as she was looking at a maximum and intended going on anyway she wisely gave the Blackwood reply, leaving Sally the task of settling the final contract.

Issie led the nine of diamonds. How do you fancy your chances? Which is the last suit that you intend to play? Which suit needs to be tackled early on?

Let's look at the full deal.

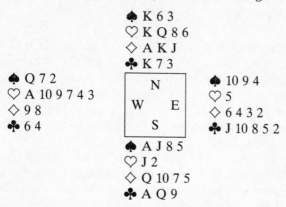

```
              ♠ K 6 3
              ♡ K Q 8 6
              ◇ A K J
              ♣ K 7 3
♠ Q 7 2                          ♠ 10 9 4
♡ A 10 9 7 4 3    N              ♡ 5
◇ 9 8          W     E           ◇ 6 4 3 2
♣ 6 4             S              ♣ J 10 8 5 2
              ♠ A J 8 5
              ♡ J 2
              ◇ Q 10 7 5
              ♣ A Q 9
```

With eleven tricks on top, the chances of finding one more must be pretty good. A simple spade finesse could be the answer, but this is the suit to play last of all, since first it is necessary to collect the data. Knocking out the ace of hearts is an early priority.

Aunt Agatha gave a smooth performance. She won the diamond in dummy and played a heart to her knave. West won and continued diamonds. The diamond winners were cashed, and Issie discarded well when parting with one heart and one spade. Dummy let go a spade. The king and queen of hearts revealed the break in this suit. More than that, they gave Mildred a chance to discard poorly. She parted with one club and one spade, while Aunt Agatha threw the five of spades. Three rounds of clubs completed the exact count, and declarer now cashed the king and ace of spades, felling Issie's queen, with the authority of a player who knew all the answers.

'You know,' said Aunt Agatha, giving Sally a wink, 'one should always avoid taking losing finesses, it is such an infra dig. way to concede tricks.'

THE LAST SAY

The bidding raises an interesting point. Should the bid of 4 NT be quantitative or ace-asking? On balance the quantitative tag is more useful, since it is then possible both to enquire about a fit and, when none is found, to make a quantitative slam try in case partner is maximum. If you strike a major fit, and have slam aspirations, it is usually possible to bid four of a minor prior to inquiring about aces.

As to the play—Issie did well to foresee that he would eventually have to part with a spade and thus let one go early on, just as though he had not a care in the world. It could be argued that such a far-seeing discard was suspicious—even naive—but arguments about bluff and double bluff can go on interminably. Generally the casual, anticipated approach is better than the enforced wriggle. Mildred, on the other hand, should have clung to her three spades as she would to her skirts on a windy day. She didn't need three spades, but she did need to camouflage the position. Incidentally, Mildred didn't need more than three clubs. Aunt Agatha had already shown up with four diamonds and had announced a four-card spade suit via Stayman, so she could not hold more than three clubs herself. Once Mildred had revealed her secret Aunt Agatha knew the spades were going to fall because the count of the hand was complete.

With Aunt Agatha out of the room for a moment, Issie took the opportunity to speak with some feeling about her run of success. 'It's uncanny how your aunt keeps pulling out cards without making the semblance of a mistake,' he complained. This somewhat ungallant appraisal was followed by another piece of typical bridge-player's hyperbole as Issie continued: 'That is to say, when she is my opponent.' I was about to step in and defend Aunt Agatha—although she is the last person in the world to need a Sir Galahad—when Issie was off again. 'She is always saying how lucky I am, but I think she leads a charmed existence—the Blarney Stone personified.'

The sudden silence heralded Aunt Agatha's return. Although she made no comment there was an amused glint in her eye, and I am sure she knew that she had been the subject of the conversation. Anyway it was down to business again. After a few uneventful hands this one cropped up.

N–S game
Dealer South

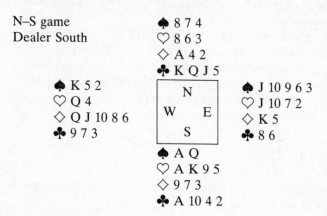

```
                    ♠ 8 7 4
                    ♡ 8 6 3
                    ◇ A 4 2
                    ♣ K Q J 5
  ♠ K 5 2          ┌─────────┐      ♠ J 10 9 6 3
  ♡ Q 4            │    N    │      ♡ J 10 7 2
  ◇ Q J 10 8 6     │  W   E  │      ◇ K 5
  ♣ 9 7 3          │    S    │      ♣ 8 6
                   └─────────┘
                    ♠ A Q
                    ♡ A K 9 5
                    ◇ 9 7 3
                    ♣ A 10 4 2
```

The bidding:

S	W	N	E
(A. A.)	(Issie)	(Sally)	(Mildred)
1 ♡	No	2 ♣	No
3 NT	No	No	No

Issie led the queen of diamonds, and when dummy played low Mildred won with the king so as to avoid blocking the suit. A diamond was returned at trick two, which Aunt Agatha won with the ace. She now played three rounds of clubs, East discarding the knave of spades. It looked as if East had started with only four cards in the minors, so Aunt Agatha cashed the ace and king of hearts before taking her fourth club, on which both opponents discarded spades. Assessing the situation correctly, Aunt Agatha exited with her last diamond and was subsequently able to collect the final two spade tricks for her contract.

'Well played, partner!' cried Sally excitedly. 'When I looked at Issie's hand and saw the king of spades was wrong I never thought you'd make it.'

'Make it, my foot,' moaned Issie ungraciously. 'If my partner has the wit to return a spade at trick two the contract has about as much chance as a Communist candidate in a by-election at Bournemouth.'

'Oh, I had to return your suit and get it established,' countered Mildred. 'It's one of the rules.' Mildred is one of those players who works to a pattern. She follows the traditional line as well as she can, but anything slightly off-key is beyond her. For her to have switched was about as probable as a five-pound note in the Sunday-morning collection.

THE LAST SAY

Issie's criticism was not entirely justified. Suppose the South and West cards are like this:

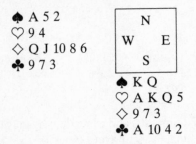

```
♠ A 5 2            ┌─────────┐
♡ 9 4              │    N    │
◇ Q J 10 8 6       │  W   E  │
♣ 9 7 3            │    S    │
                   └─────────┘
        ♠ K Q
        ♡ A K Q 5
        ◇ 9 7 3
        ♣ A 10 4 2
```

Now a spade return from East would establish declarer's ninth trick.

Full marks to Aunt Agatha for reading the distribution correctly. West might have had the knave of hearts instead of the king of spades, in which case the spade finesse would have been the winning play. However, when the queen of hearts dropped, the theory of restricted choice suggested that the knave was with East.

Aunt Agatha was still basking in the glory of success when the next rubber started. However, it was not long before her partner incurred her displeasure. The line-up was Aunt Agatha and Mildred against Sally and Issie. This was the hand that caused the trouble.

Love all
Dealer West

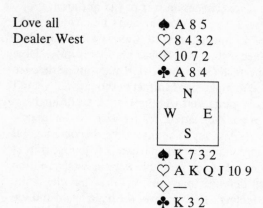

♠ A 8 5
♡ 8 4 3 2
♢ 10 7 2
♣ A 8 4

♠ K 7 3 2
♡ A K Q J 10 9
♢ —
♣ K 3 2

The bidding:

| S | W | N | E |
(Mildred)	(Sally)	(A. A.)	(Issie)
—	3 NT	No	4 ♢
4 ♡	No	5 ♣	No
5 ♢	No	6 ♡	No
No	No		

Unfortunately Mildred made only eleven tricks and that is what got Aunt Agatha on the war-path. 'Partner,' she exclaimed, obviously using the title loosely, 'you had a marvellous opportunity to draw a delicate inference from the bidding and Issie's defence. Don't you ever consider the little things at the bridge table?'

'But there was no way of making it you know, Agatha dear,' countered Mildred somewhat querulously, while at the same time avoiding a direct answer to the question. (Maybe she learnt that trick from watching politicians being interviewed on TV. They always seem to reply to an awkward question with something like, 'Well, I would just like to say this . . .' 'This' may turn out to be practically anything the speaker feels the urge to get out of his system, except an answer to the question.)

Issie had been longing to get a word in, and while Aunt Agatha was eyeing Mildred in much the same way as a cat regards a mouse when it has it cornered, he grabbed his opportunity. 'How on earth could my perfectly straightforward and routine defence have helped Mildred to make her contract? I thought Sally and I played an impeccable game and were rewarded accordingly.'

Aunt Agatha turned her attention to Issie, momentarily forgetting her mouse. Although she may never become a good politician it is difficult to fault her when it comes to giving a direct answer. 'It was the fact that you probably were playing a routine and straightforward defence that provided the vital clue,' she retorted with some feeling. 'Let's go over the hand again and see just how impeccable you were.'

Warming to her task as Chief Director of Ops, Aunt Agatha summarized the auction. 'It was clear from the bidding that Sally had little more than a solid diamond suit and that Issie was too weak to allow 3 NT to stand. Mildred made a natural bid of 4 $\heartsuit$, and I reckoned my two aces would be invaluable, hence my cue bid of 5 ♣. When Mildred showed a diamond void I could hardly do less than bid the slam.

'The ace of diamonds was led and ruffed, East following with the three. Two rounds of trumps were played, West following suit and East discarding the five of diamonds on the second round. Eleven tricks were easy—six hearts, two clubs, two spades and a spade ruff in dummy. But to make her contract Mildred saw that she needed to ruff a club in dummy which of course necessitated a 3–3 spade break. Ignoring the wise maxim, "little things mean a lot", she embarked on this play, only to find the spades 4–2 and her contract on the floor.'

This was the full hand:

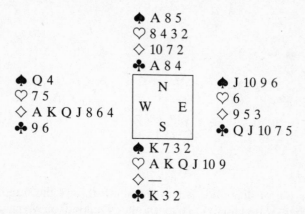

```
                    ♠ A 8 5
                    ♡ 8 4 3 2
                    ◇ 10 7 2
                    ♣ A 8 4
 ♠ Q 4                  N                 ♠ J 10 9 6
 ♡ 7 5                                    ♡ 6
 ◇ A K Q J 8 6 4    W       E             ◇ 9 5 3
 ♣ 9 6                  S                 ♣ Q J 10 7 5
                    ♠ K 7 3 2
                    ♡ A K Q J 10 9
                    ◇ —
                    ♣ K 3 2
```

Aunt Agatha continued: 'Since Sally was marked with seven diamonds and two hearts she would need a singleton club if the spades were to divide 3–3. That means that Issie would have not less than six clubs. Agreed?' The others nodded their heads. 'So, playing a straightforward and routine defence, do you not think it likely that Issie would throw one of his six clubs on the second round of hearts?' Not waiting for a reply, Aunt Agatha went on, 'A slender clue, I admit, but certainly the best one available and far better than putting your shirt on the unlikely spade break.'

'But I can't see any other chance,' said Mildred. 'If the spades fail to break you must go down, and that's all there is to it.'

Aunt Agatha had a determined note in her voice as she took command once more. 'Really, Mildred? Then try this line of play for size. You draw the second trump, cash the king and ace of spades, ruff the seven of diamonds and then cash the king and ace of clubs. You are now in dummy and this is the position:

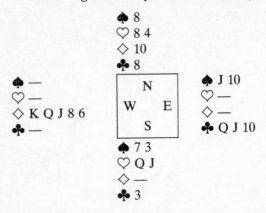

'The ten of diamonds is led and South throws the three of clubs. Sally wins and has to play another diamond, on which you discard the eight of spades from dummy while you ruff it in your own hand. The remainder of the tricks are taken on a crossruff. Small slam made.'

'But—' began Mildred.

'But nothing,' interrupted Aunt Agatha. 'There is no law against a player holding a 2–2–7–2 shape, so even if you couldn't read the small print the partial elimination and throw-in, with loser on loser, was just as viable as your plan—to rely on a 3–3 spade break. And much more elegant.'

'Oh well, I was right about one thing,' said Issie. 'If the contract was cold all the time at least our play was impeccable.'

Aunt Agatha glared in Issie's direction, 'Wrong again,' she snapped. 'Just tell me how you make the contract if Sally leads anything but a diamond.'

Who said bridge was a family game?

THE LAST SAY

Of course, Aunt Agatha was right. So often there are clues available from both the bidding and the play if only one listens carefully and observes what happens. The fact that a player fails to make a certain bid or play may be just as important as what he actually does. Had Issie held six clubs on the above hand it is not certain that he would have discarded one, but it seems a likely thing to do. The fact that he chose a diamond instead affords the presumption that he might have considered a club discard dangerous.

Perhaps Aunt Agatha was influenced by the fact that her partner was the timorous Mildred, because on the next hand she certainly seemed to get the bit between her teeth.

Love all
Dealer South

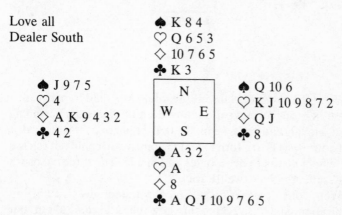

```
                    ♠ K 8 4
                    ♡ Q 6 5 3
                    ◇ 10 7 6 5
                    ♣ K 3
    ♠ J 9 7 5              N        ♠ Q 10 6
    ♡ 4                             ♡ K J 10 9 8 7 2
    ◇ A K 9 4 3 2   W       E       ◇ Q J
    ♣ 4 2                           ♣ 8
                         S
                    ♠ A 3 2
                    ♡ A
                    ◇ 8
                    ♣ A Q J 10 9 7 6 5
```

The bidding:

S	W	N	E
(A. A.)	(Sally)	(Mildred)	(Issie)
2 ♣	No	2 NT	3 ♡
4 ♣	No	5 ♣	No
6 ♣	No	No	No

Sally led the ace of diamonds and studied Issie's queen with interest. Eventually she decided that Aunt Agatha would not have bid the slam with two losing diamonds and she switched to the four of hearts. Declarer won in hand, perforce, drew trumps finishing in dummy, and ruffed a diamond. She now reeled off all her trumps. This was the position before the last club was played:

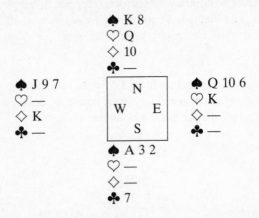

```
                    ♠ K 8
                    ♡ Q
                    ◇ 10
                    ♣ —
    ♠ J 9 7        ┌─────────┐      ♠ Q 10 6
    ♡ —           │    N    │      ♡ K
    ◇ K           │  W   E  │      ◇ —
    ♣ —           │    S    │      ♣ —
                  └─────────┘
                    ♠ A 3 2
                    ♡ —
                    ◇ —
                    ♣ 7
```

When the seven of clubs hit the table West had to part with a spade in order to prevent dummy's ten of diamonds becoming good. Having earned its keep, the ten of diamonds was discarded and now it was East's turn to feel the pinch. He could not release his king of hearts so he, too, let go a spade. The three of spades was Aunt Agatha's twelfth trick.

'Well done, partner!' exclaimed Mildred, eyes shining in admiration. She wasn't quite sure how it had all come about, but Aunt Agatha looked as though she had played a fine game and Mildred was only too happy to go along with that.

'Nothing we can do about it,' chimed in Issie. 'Agatha pushed the boat out and found all the luck running with her, as usual.'

Aunt Agatha seemed about to say something but then thought better of it, no doubt content with her moment of glory.

THE LAST SAY

South has an awkward opening bid. There is something to be said for a simple 1 ♣, which is unlikely to get passed out—there must be a lot of shape about— but it may not be so easy to catch up in the later rounds. The alternative, 2 ♣, appears to be something of a stretch.

I have an idea that Aunt Agatha spotted the killing defence—a spade switch at trick two. It breaks the communications for a double squeeze. Although perhaps a world-class player should find this defence, it would nevertheless be an excellent play, and certainly too sophisticated for Sally.

After a few more hands there was considerable excitement when this deal came up. But first you might like to place yourself in Aunt Agatha's seat and consider your final bid as South with this hand.

The bidding:

	S	W	N	E
	(A. A.)	(Sally)	(Mildred)	(Issie)
	—	—	1 ♠	No
♠ 4	2 ♡	No	3 ♣	No
♡ A K 6 4 3	3 ◇	No	3 ♠	No
◇ K J 7 5	4 NT	No	5 ♡	No
♣ A Q 6	5 NT	No	6 ♡	No
	?			

Have you made your mind up? Here comes the full deal.

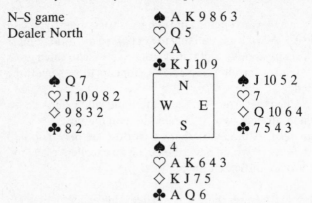

N–S game
Dealer North

♠ A K 9 8 6 3
♡ Q 5
♢ A
♣ K J 10 9

♠ Q 7
♡ J 10 9 8 2
♢ 9 8 3 2
♣ 8 2

♠ J 10 5 2
♡ 7
♢ Q 10 6 4
♣ 7 5 4 3

♠ 4
♡ A K 6 4 3
♢ K J 7 5
♣ A Q 6

Over 6 ♡ Aunt Agatha bid 7 ♣, and everyone passed.

Issie led the three of clubs and when dummy went down it was obvious that something was upsetting Mildred. What worried her most, apparently, was her partner's choice of contract. 'Seven clubs with only three-card support. That's not right, you know,' murmured Mildred in hurt tones.

'Nonsense,' replied Aunt Agatha, 'just do your best. You never know, it might even be good enough.'

Mildred shook her head sadly, and with some reluctance returned to her immediate task. She won the opening lead in her own hand with the nine of clubs, cashed the ace of spades, ruffed a spade, returned to hand with the queen of hearts and ruffed a second spade with the ace of trumps. It only remained to return to hand with the ace of diamonds, draw the trumps and claim the remainder of the tricks.

Mildred was obviously as delighted as she was surprised at the outcome of this strange hand. 'Perhaps *I* should have bid seven notrumps. That would have been a much safer contract,' she said, clearly without thinking. 'I thought you had to have four trumps to support partner's second suit. There might have been five clubs in one hand you know, Agatha dear,' she remonstrated.

'And cows might give beer,' interrupted Issie irrelevantly. 'In Agatha's present form I am only surprised the trumps didn't break $3\frac{1}{2}$–$3\frac{1}{2}$.'

Issie's remarks were more than enough to goad Aunt Agatha into action. 'You will notice,' she observed, giving Issie a withering look, 'that all the relevant suits broke badly. The clubs were 4–2, the spades 4–2 and the hearts 5–1, yet seven clubs was virtually a lay-down. In fact it was the only good grand slam. Isn't anyone going to congratulate me on my brilliant bid?'

There were general murmurs of approval, in varying degrees of enthusiasm.

THE LAST SAY

High-level contracts in a 4–3 fit are rare birds, although their plumage is quite dazzling when they appear in the right light. Aunt Agatha recognized the situation when it was clear that no normal fit could be established, yet her club holding was substantial in quality and she had ruffing values. Perhaps she was lucky to find Mildred's clubs quite as solid as they were. Nevertheless, it was a fine calculated risk.

More common is the 4–3 fit at game level when there is no alternative contract worth considering. Here is an example. Dealer West:

♠ K 9 7 4 2   ♠ Q 3
♡ A K J 7   ♡ Q 10 4
◇ Q 3   ◇ A K J 8 5 2
♣ Q 4   ♣ J 6

	N	
W		E
	S	

This would be a reasonable sequence:

W	E
1 ♠	2 ♢
2 ♡	3 ♣ *
3 ♢	3 ♡
4 ♡	

* *The fourth suit—forcing—looking for 3 NT*

As I left the scene, Aunt Agatha had taken up her favourite position. Queen of all she surveyed. The others listened as she talked. . . .

2. Aunt Agatha Goes Cruising

'It's Aunt Agatha on the phone,' announced my wife. 'She wants to come on the cruise with us—and bring Issie, too.'

'Tell her the ship has no stabilizers, the captain is a sex maniac and they have drunken orgies every night,' I replied defiantly.

'But you know none of that is true,' retorted my wife patiently.

'What on earth has that got to do with it?' I countered incredulously. 'Anybody might think you actually want Aunt Agatha on that ship. I tell you, she'll create chaos. The company will wish they'd never heard of her—or us, for that matter.'

But the battle was already lost. Aunt Agatha was determined to cruise on our ship. My wife had weakened at the vital moment, and I was not allowed anywhere near the phone. 'You'll only upset everyone while lying your head off,' was how she so charmingly put it. Anyway, it is now history that Aunt Agatha and Issie did join our bridge cruise, but I am reasonably certain that all those concerned have never been quite the same since that memorable occasion. Her cabin was on the wrong side, her ticket was too expensive, the porthole wouldn't open and the food was not up to standard. She was kept awake at night by yahoos doing the cha-cha-cha, or whatever, and the staff were never there when she wanted them. The weather was too hot, the air-conditioning too cold, the bridge-players and her cards too bad . . . and so it went on. But it was in the bridge room itself that the fireworks really went off with a bang.

Of course, the standard was very mixed, as is inevitable on board ship, and Aunt Agatha soon found that her partners were not always up to following her own impeccable moves. This hand was a case in point.

N–S game

Dealer South

♠ K 7 4
♡ 10 2
♢ K Q 10 7
♣ A 7 4 3

```
        N
   W        E
        S
```

♠ A 6
♡ A 7
♢ A J 9 6 4
♣ Q 6 5 2

The bidding:

S	W	N	E
(Issie)			(A. A.)
1 ♢	No	2 ♣	4 ♠
5 ♣	Dble	5 ♢	Dble
No	No	No	

West led the five of spades. How should declarer plan the play?

Obviously East has a lot of shape, probably seven spades, the top hearts and an extreme shortage in clubs. But why the double? It is certainly not based on trumps or top tricks. So . . . ? Of course, it must mean a club void. To make the contract, therefore, declarer will need a little luck with the heart suit and that ten in dummy may yet be a blessing. This was the full deal:

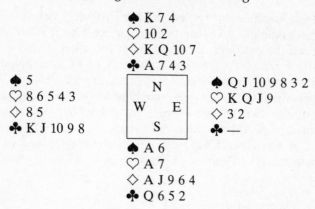

Issie won the spade lead in his hand, took two rounds of trumps, cashed the ace of hearts, the king of spades and ruffed a spade. He now played his last heart to dummy's ten. Aunt Agatha had to win this trick and of course couldn't avoid conceding a ruff and discard. This was the position as Aunt Agatha took her first trick:

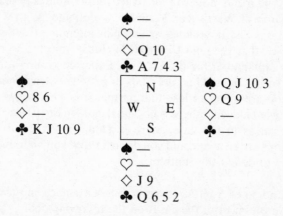

Aunt Agatha led the queen of hearts. Issie threw a club from his own hand and ruffed in dummy. Now a small club from both hands left West helpless.

Aunt Agatha was sorely peeved at her partner's failure to lead a club originally. 'Anyone but a complete moron would have realized the position,' she muttered in just audible tones.

'But I thought . . .' began West, only to be interrupted by Aunt Agatha's testy comment: 'That's just the trouble. Bad players shouldn't think—they should just follow their partners!'

Issie also had something to say, but he chose to do this at a safe distance from Aunt Agatha. 'You know,' he confided to me, 'if there is one thing I like better than end-playing one of my opponents, it's to end-play both of them in turn.'

THE LAST SAY

A point that seems to have escaped everyone's notice was West's fatuous double of 5 ♣. With a featureless hand, except for strong clubs, and a partner who at favourable vulnerability proclaimed only the values for a pre-emptive bid, there was a strong case for lying low. If indeed West does pass, North may well do likewise and that will mean money in the bank. More dubious perhaps is the question of West's lead against 5 ◇ doubled. With a little foresight it is easy to visualize an end-play looming, and it is also easy to see that East must be void in clubs. There is no other rational explanation for the bidding. Experience shows that a partner who is denied his ruff tends to get highly frustrated, so unless you are about to lose that partner it is wise to give him what he wants, even if there is no actual gain on the transaction. Sometimes, as in this case, there is a dual reward: partner's frustrations are relieved, and you discover that you've found the only way to defeat the contract.

A few hands later Aunt Agatha was restored to good spirits when she made the most of the cards on the following deal:

Game all
Dealer South

♠ A J 9 5
♡ Q 5 4
♢ A 10 5 4
♣ A 10

♠ K Q 10 8 7
♡ A 6
♢ Q J 7 2
♣ K 4

This was the bidding, with Aunt Agatha sitting South:

S	N
1 ♠	3 ♣
3 ♢	3 ♠
4 NT	5 ♠
5 NT	6 ♣
6 ♠	

West led the knave of hearts, which was covered by the queen, king and ace. Aunt Agatha drew trumps in three rounds, West following to the first and then discarding the seven of hearts and two of clubs. The queen of diamonds won the next trick, East following with the nine, but when Aunt Agatha tried the knave of diamonds West covered and East threw the three of clubs. How should declarer proceed?

This was the full hand:

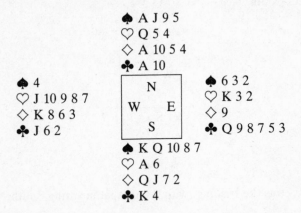

Aunt Agatha was quick to see that her only chance was a squeeze and throw-in play. After two top clubs and one more round of trumps this was the position, with South to play:

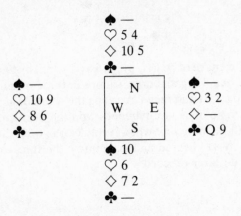

When Aunt Agatha led the ten of spades West had to part with a heart. Dummy and East also threw hearts. Aunt Agatha now performed the *coup de grâce* when she threw West in with the ten of hearts to lead up to the split diamond tenace.

Aunt Agatha was clearly delighted with the outcome of this hand, but satisfied herself with the laconic comment: 'Wouldn't have bid it without the seven of diamonds . . . naturally!'

THE LAST SAY

Aunt Agatha was lucky that all the pips were working in her favour: the nine of diamonds dropped, and all the intermediate hearts were with West. Nevertheless, her play was impeccable —well, almost impeccable. A low diamond at trick five instead of the queen would have been a slight improvement, inserting dummy's ten when West plays low. The point is that West might have had the singleton king of diamonds. Improbable, perhaps, for that would have given her a very odd shape, but by no means impossible.

I am not quite clear why North forced with three clubs rather than three diamonds. Players tend to do this sort of thing, but the logic of it is hard to follow. Still, it was a good decision to jump immediately, since the controls and fit are so powerful.

The kibitzers really enjoyed this hand and it was noticeable that everyone showed Aunt Agatha a little more respect after her dazzling performance. However, Aunt Agatha was out of luck on the next offering when playing 3 NT against Issie. As so often happens, Issie's guardian angel was working overtime on this occasion.

Love all
Dealer East

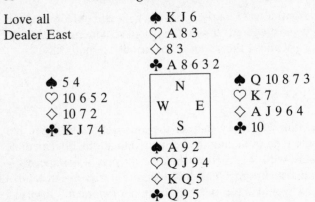

```
                    ♠ K J 6
                    ♡ A 8 3
                    ♢ 8 3
                    ♣ A 8 6 3 2
   ♠ 5 4          ┌─────────┐        ♠ Q 10 8 7 3
   ♡ 10 6 5 2     │    N    │        ♡ K 7
   ♢ 10 7 2       │  W   E  │        ♢ A J 9 6 4
   ♣ K J 7 4      │    S    │        ♣ 10
                  └─────────┘
                    ♠ A 9 2
                    ♡ Q J 9 4
                    ♢ K Q 5
                    ♣ Q 9 5
```

   The bidding was straightforward. East passed, and Aunt
Agatha (South) opened 1 NT, which her partner raised to 3 NT.
   Issie (West) led the two of hearts, which was won by the king.
East now switched to the six of diamonds, which Aunt Agatha
won in her hand. A club to dummy's ace and a club return to
South's queen, East discarding the seven of spades, gave Issie the
lead once more. Without much thought Issie played the ten of
diamonds, and it was at this point that his guardian angel put in
such spirited work on his behalf. East, who was a notoriously
careless and absent-minded player, covered with the knave of
diamonds, and then, sensing that something was wrong, said:
'The ten was against me, wasn't it?' Hearing that it was Issie's
ten, East apologized profusely, little knowing the strength and
determination of Issie's guardian angel. When Aunt Agatha
cashed her heart winners, East was now sufficiently alerted to the
dangers of a throw-in play, there having been so much discussion
about the diamond suit, so she parted with a second spade and
the *nine* of diamonds. This was the end position with South to
play, needing three more tricks for her contract. The defence
have two tricks.

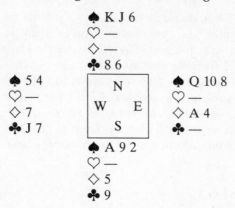

```
                    ♠ K J 6
                    ♡ —
                    ◇ —
                    ♣ 8 6
    ♠ 5 4        ┌─────────┐     ♠ Q 10 8
    ♡ —          │    N    │     ♡ —
    ◇ 7          │  W   E  │     ◇ A 4
    ♣ J 7        │    S    │     ♣ —
                 └─────────┘
                    ♠ A 9 2
                    ♡ —
                    ◇ 5
                    ♣ 9
```

As you can see, declarer is in an awkward spot. If she plays a club, West will win and then put his partner in to cash the last two diamonds. If she tries the spade finesse there will be no joy there. We come then to the diamond suit. Partly by accident and partly by design East has left the position fluid. She can take both the diamond tricks or leave her partner on lead with the seven. Had she retained either the knave or the nine, instead of the four, she would have been unable to avoid the end-play.

From South's angle, two factors emerged. First, it seemed probable that East guarded the spades, as she had petered and was obviously marked with length. Secondly, the four of diamonds had never appeared. Could it be that East had led the fifth highest diamond originally (from A J 9 7 6) and West now held the four? Anyway, deciding that there was no better chance Aunt Agatha played her five of diamonds. When West followed with the seven, and not the four, a new problem arose: what should declarer discard from dummy? If a club is selected, East can leave her partner on lead to cash the last two clubs. If a spade is thrown, East can overtake, cash the thirteenth diamond and exit safely with a spade. In fact Aunt Agatha chose a spade, but East made no mistake as she cashed her winning diamonds and exited with the eight of spades.

Issie was in raptures about this hand, but I couldn't help

feeling the lavish praise he heaped on his partner for her stylish unblocking play was more to annoy Aunt Agatha than to award his partner with an Oscar. Discussing this deal later on, Aunt Agatha quite correctly pointed out that she could have made her contract by playing the club suit differently; a low club towards the queen, subsequently finessing West for the knave. But what really upset her was losing her contract to—as she put it—'A dizzy female who just pulled out cards haphazardly and then wallowed in unwarranted praise from that ass Issie.'

THE LAST SAY

It is perhaps something of an esoteric point, but maybe Aunt Agatha should have directed her mind to this question: who was more likely to have length in clubs and how would it affect the play? As West selected the two of hearts for his opening lead, showing a four-card suit, and East was presumably long in diamonds, perhaps West was more likely to hold long clubs. If Aunt Agatha arrives at this conclusion then a heart to dummy's ace at trick three followed by a low club towards the queen is the correct play. The point is that the minor-tenace holding of the ♣ A 8 will then be situated over the remaining key cards.

As so often happens after a set-back, Aunt Agatha wasted little time in bouncing back to form.

E–W game
Dealer West

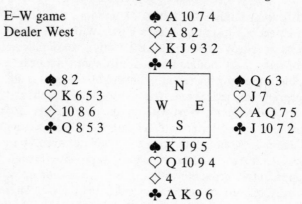

♠ A 10 7 4
♡ A 8 2
◇ K J 9 3 2
♣ 4

♠ 8 2
♡ K 6 5 3
◇ 10 8 6
♣ Q 8 5 3

♠ Q 6 3
♡ J 7
◇ A Q 7 5
♣ J 10 7 2

♠ K J 9 5
♡ Q 10 9 4
◇ 4
♣ A K 9 6

This was the strange bidding sequence:

S	W	N	E
(A. A.)			
—	No	1 ◇	No
1 ♡	No	2 ♡	No
3 NT	No	No	No

West led the three of clubs, and as North revealed her secrets Aunt Agatha glared in total disbelief. Game in spades was virtually a lay-down, while 3 NT might easily hit the deck. What a life! Despite her inner smouldering Aunt Agatha quickly adopted a poker-face, but those who know her well would have sensed that an eruption was imminent. Meantime, having murmured a 'Thank you, partner' which had a notable ring of insincerity about it, she captured East's ten of clubs with her ace and led a heart. She realized that success would depend on guessing the position of the queen of spades and, probably, bringing in three heart tricks. In order to achieve the first objective it was obviously going to help if the distribution of the heart suit could be verified. Furthermore, the double finesse in hearts, clearly the odds play, would obviate a hideous guess in the event of East holding more than a doubleton. So trick two

went to East's knave of hearts (4, 3, 8, J), and the two of clubs
was returned, the six losing to West's eight. Without looking
sufficiently far ahead, West now made the costly error of playing
the queen of clubs. East thought momentarily about unblocking
the knave, but settled for the seven. Aunt Agatha, who was not
slow to interpret East's indecision, won with the king of clubs and
then endeavoured to tempt West with the queen of hearts. But
West ducked, and on the third round of hearts East discarded the
seven of diamonds. Although the heart suit had not lived up to
expectations, Aunt Agatha had compiled an impressive dossier.
West had apparently started life with four hearts and four clubs,
so was more likely to be short in spades than East. That
determined the play of the spade suit—although four spades, two
hearts and two clubs totalled only eight tricks. However, after
the ace of spades, ten of spades and king of spades this was the
position with South to play:

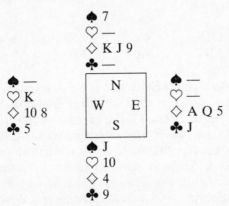

On the knave of spades West threw the five of clubs, but East
was far from comfortable. She badly wanted to ditch the knave of
clubs but was now positive that that would only make Aunt
Agatha's task several degrees easier—so she settled for the five
of diamonds. In a flash Aunt Agatha whipped out the nine of
clubs and East groaned audibly, telling Aunt Agatha all she
wanted to know.

For the moment the bizarre bidding sequence was forgotten as North–South chalked up the game, but it was inevitable that someone would say something about it sooner or later.

'You played that hand jolly well,' said North admiringly. And then, as an afterthought, 'But I don't know why you didn't try your spade suit over my two hearts.'

Aunt Agatha's eyes narrowed menacingly 'just like a laser beam on heat', as Issie once described that famous penetrating glare. It was one thing to congratulate Aunt Agatha—she could take any amount of hero worship—but it was a totally different cup of tea to criticize her. Only the brave, or foolhardy, attempted it. Like a viper about to strike, Aunt Agatha replied, 'I didn't bid spades because I knew that if you only had three hearts you could not possibly hold four spades.'

'Oh no, dear,' countered North authoritatively. 'I must limit my hand. I only had twelve points, you see.'

The battle raged for some time until East insisted on getting on with the next hand.

THE LAST SAY

In a sense this hand was a chapter of accidents. First of all there was that idiotic bidding sequence. Why North should need to distort her rebid is beyond me. Her claim that she was minimum and therefore had to rebid 2 ♡ is reminiscent of bridge in the Dark Ages. Of course, *if* one accepts that North's bidding was rational (Heaven forbid), then South was wrong not to introduce her spade suit. However, one should remember that every time one goes in for the pretty painting syndrome—'daisy-picking', as Hugh Kelsey so aptly calls it—one gives valuable information to the enemy. Pretty pictures, or even daisy-chains, may be very attractive but they do nothing for a bridge-player if there is no possibility of gain. All they achieve is something positive for the defence—like a detailed plan of the opposition's strengths, weaknesses and disposition.

One of Aunt Agatha's most memorable hands occurred when
she was in opposition to my occasional team-mate and great
friend of many years' standing, former European champion Nico
Gardener. Consider Nico's problem on the following hand
where he is the declarer (South) and Aunt Agatha sits West.

N–S game
Dealer South

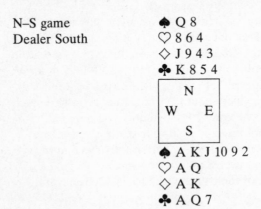

    ♠ Q 8
    ♡ 8 6 4
    ◇ J 9 4 3
    ♣ K 8 5 4

    ♠ A K J 10 9 2
    ♡ A Q
    ◇ A K
    ♣ A Q 7

Aggressive bidding landed South in 7 ♠, against which Aunt
Agatha led the six of spades. Prospects appear good. With twelve
tricks on top the thirteenth could come from the club break, the
heart finesse, a squeeze or the possibility of bringing down the
queen of diamonds in three rounds. Not surprisingly, Nico got to
work so as to combine all the various chances.

Tricks two and three went to the two top diamonds, everyone
following. But on the second round of spades, won in dummy,
East threw the two of hearts. Nico now ruffed a diamond, but
then a funny thing happened: Aunt Agatha did not follow to the
third round of diamonds, nor did she discard. She underruffed!
Nico, a model of correctness and imperturbability, did not twitch
a muscle; he regarded this development with the composure of a
player who has seen it all before. What he hadn't seen before was
Aunt Agatha, the benign little old lady sitting on his left, looking
somewhat frail and as innocent as the calm blue waters over
which we rode so majestically.

Anyway, Nico drew the last trump and played his penultimate trump, West discarding the ten of hearts and East the three of hearts and the eight of diamonds. He then cashed the ace and queen of clubs, everyone following, to leave this position:

```
        ♠ —
        ♡ 8
        ◇ J
        ♣ K 8
      ┌─────────┐
      │    N    │
      │ W     E │
      │    S    │
      └─────────┘
        ♠ 10
        ♡ A Q
        ◇ —
        ♣ 7
```

On the ten of spades West discarded the knave of hearts, and it was now time to face the vital question. What was West up to? Had she really been squeezed, in which case she now held the knave and ten of clubs and the bare king of hearts, or was she spoofing with only one of the club honours and the guarded king of hearts? If the latter, it was essential that Nico retained both his clubs in dummy. If the former, then it would be best to discard the eight of clubs in order to put pressure on East in the red suits so that he would know how to play the hearts.

In fact Nico decided that his interests were best served by discarding the knave of diamonds from dummy. But before we look at the three-card ending let's see the full hand:

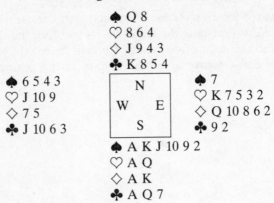

Now the three-card ending:

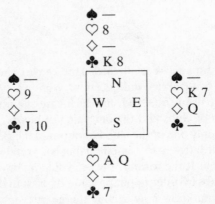

When Nico played his last club to the king, East threw the queen of diamonds. The jigsaw was now complete except for one tiny detail. Who had the king of hearts? Was it blank with West or did East have it guarded. After only a few seconds' thought Nico took the finesse and he was home.

Aunt Agatha seemed a little disgruntled at Nico's success, but mellowed when he congratulated her on a spirited defence. I am not sure that he really meant it, but to Aunt Agatha praise from Nico was praise indeed.

THE LAST SAY

Aunt Agatha's antics might well have succeeded against a lesser player than Nico Gardener, but in the final analysis South has to ask himself this question: what sort of player would send out distress signals as early as trick five, when it is quite unnecessary, with this holding: ♠ 6 5 4 3 ♡ K J 10 ◇ 7 5 ♣ J 10 6 3? That is what West would have South believe she held. In fact a good player with these cards would surely discard the ten and knave of hearts, in the same way as she might holding the J 10 9, but she certainly wouldn't want to alert declarer to her discomfiture. No doubt this argument swayed Nico's final decision, apart from the fact that the odds are distinctly in favour of the finesse.

Of course, if Aunt Agatha *had* held the king of hearts and four clubs, and defeated Nico, she would have had a story to dine out on for many months. Still, the things that might have been in bridge are legion.

A passing thought just strikes me, unworthy though it may be: I wonder if Aunt Agatha did in fact amend her heart holding to include the king and dine out on the story of Nico's downfall? She talked so much about the possibility of holding the king of hearts that in the end she might have believed that she actually held it. Sorry, Aunt Agatha, if I've done you an injustice.

Aunt Agatha was faced with another awkward hand a few deals later, this time as declarer.

Game all   ♠ A K 7 2
Dealer North   ♡ 10 9 5
                 ◇ A K Q 7 4 3
                 ♣ —

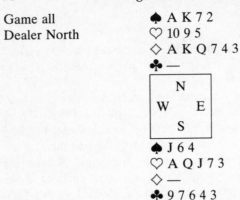

                 ♠ J 6 4
                 ♡ A Q J 7 3
                 ◇ —
                 ♣ 9 7 6 4 3

The bidding:

S	W	N	E
(A. A.)			
—	—	1 ◇	2 ♣
Dble	No	3 ♣	No
3 ♡	No	4 ♡	No
6 ♡	No	No	No

They certainly bid their values to the hilt, but even allowing for bad breaks declarer is in with a chance. How would you plan the play against the lead of the queen of clubs?

Aunt Agatha decided that she would have little chance if the king of hearts was wrong, so made her plan on the basis that it was held by East—a reasonable assumption, remembering East's vulnerable overcall. She further decided that if the diamonds didn't break favourably she would need a squeeze, so her first move was to duck the queen of clubs, throwing a spade from dummy, to rectify the count.

This was the full hand:

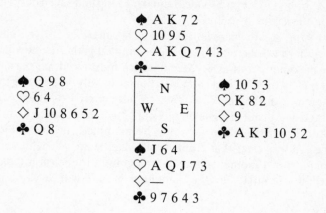

West continued a club, which was trumped in dummy. The hearts were picked up successfully, and now a spade to the ace, three top diamonds and a diamond ruff left the following position:

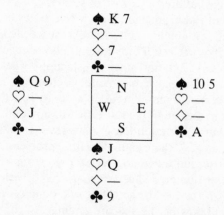

When Aunt Agatha played the queen of hearts the defenders were caught in a simultaneous double squeeze. West was forced to throw a spade, so the now useless seven of diamonds was discarded from dummy. East could not spare the ace of clubs so he, too, had to let go a spade. Dummy's king and seven of spades took the last two tricks.

If Aunt Agatha had not fully made her mark before this hand then there was no doubt that the assembled gathering now held her in some sort of awe. 'Magnificent,' murmured her partner, not quite sure what had happened but intuitively recognizing that magic was in the air. The only sour note came from East, who looked sulky and disbelieving. 'Could have made seven had she ruffed the first club in dummy,' he mumbled, in just audible tones. It was clear that Aunt Agatha had heard all right, and I thought for a moment that she was going to unleash a typical vitriolic outburst, but she contented herself with a withering look.

THE LAST SAY

Of course, East was talking nonsense, just as players so often do when they have suffered this sort of set-back. Thirteen tricks were simply not there. Indeed, even twelve tricks are far from cast-iron, and although Aunt Agatha succeeded she was certainly not foot perfect. True, her end-play was both elegant and effective and gave her much satisfaction. Also, her plan meant that she did not have to guess the position of the queen of spades. However, the best line of play is to ruff the club in dummy and run the ten of hearts. East will no doubt duck and now declarer turns her attention to diamonds. If the diamonds are no worse than 5–2 there should be little problem, but in fact East ruffs the second diamond, declarer overruffs and trumps another club in dummy. She returns to hand with a second diamond ruff and cashes the ace of hearts, dummy discarding a spade. This will now be the six-card ending:

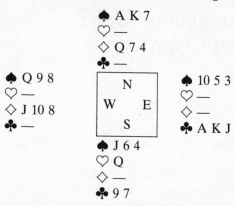

♠ A K 7
♡ —
♢ Q 7 4
♣ —

♠ Q 9 8   ♠ 10 5 3
♡ —   ♡ —
♢ J 10 8   ♢ —
♣ —   ♣ A K J

N
W   E
S

♠ J 6 4
♡ Q
♢ —
♣ 9 7

The count is now complete. West is known to hold three spades and three diamonds and East three spades and three clubs, but it is important for declarer to make up her mind about the position of the queen of spades. If she places it with West, then she must play the queen of hearts. This will force a diamond discard (dummy also discards a diamond), and now the ace of spades, the queen of diamonds and seven of diamonds will end-play West. If declarer decides that it is East who holds the queen of spades, then dummy is entered with the ace of spades and the queen of diamonds is cashed, East and South discarding clubs. Now a diamond ruff forces East to part with his penultimate club so that he can be thrown in with declarer's last club to lead away from ♠ Q x.

When I showed this alternative ending to Aunt Agatha she rather took the wind out of my sails by saying, 'Now perhaps you understand why I played for the double squeeze. I don't like having to guess the position of key cards. I would rather the opponents did the work for me.' I looked at her closely. Had she really considered the hand so deeply, I wondered. I thought I detected a slight twinkle in her eye, but she turned her gaze away to contemplate the calm blue sea.

3. Aunt Agatha Meets Jeremy Flint

'What are you doing on Wednesday?' asked Aunt Agatha nonchalantly.

Being careful and diplomatic by nature, evasive and non-committal by experience, I was equal to the test. There was no need to invent a mountaineering expedition to Wales, or a bird-watching excursion to those beautiful islands off the west coast of Scotland, for I had just fixed up to have a day's racing with Jeremy Flint. 'I'm going racing with Jeremy,' I replied, relieved to be able to escape by giving an absolutely truthful answer.

'Where *is* racing on Wednesday?' continued my aunt. The purposeful note in her voice had an ominous ring, and for a moment I was tempted to reply Hamilton Park, Ayr or Sedgefield, the most distant racecourses I could recall offhand. But then I remembered that Aunt Agatha took more than a little interest in racing herself, and she would certainly check, even if she did not actually know already.

'Er . . . Lingfield Park,' I replied hesitantly.

'That couldn't be better then,' chortled Aunt Agatha, 'because Issie and Mildred are coming in and they want a game of bridge. You and Jeremy can make up the four—with me too, of course. The stakes will be a little lower than Jeremy likes, no doubt, but we shall be playing the big game on Wednesday.'

Aunt Agatha's idea of a 'big game' is about 10 pence a hundred, and I didn't relish breaking the news to Jeremy. What should be my approach, I wondered? The casual line: 'We've got a very special invitation on Wednesday, Jeremy. Dinner and bridge with my aunt. She's longing to meet you.' Alternatively, the challenging threat: 'After racing on Wednesday Aunt

Agatha wants to take a little money off you at bridge. She thinks you're scared.' Or perhaps the sardonic: 'If you are prepared to risk an inquiry by the Gaming Board, Aunt Agatha wants us to attend her "Las Vegas" night. That means bridge at high stakes—in her own private den of iniquity. Dress formal, plus cheque-book.'

I forget exactly how the conversation went, but I don't think it was anything to do with my cajoling, or powers of persuasion, that got Jeremy seated at Aunt Agatha's bridge table. It was Jeremy's sheer curiosity. With his suspicious mind he had always been sceptical about Aunt Agatha, maintaining that she just had to be a figment of my imagination. He now knows better.

In the first rubber Jeremy and Issie cut together against Aunt Agatha and Mildred. After a few deals the cards fell like this.

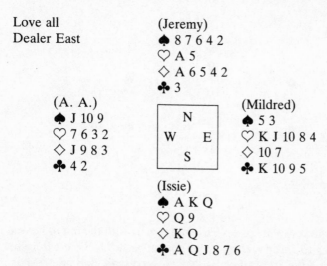

Love all
Dealer East

(Jeremy)
♠ 8 7 6 4 2
♡ A 5
♢ A 6 5 4 2
♣ 3

(A. A.)
♠ J 10 9
♡ 7 6 3 2
♢ J 9 8 3
♣ 4 2

(Mildred)
♠ 5 3
♡ K J 10 8 4
♢ 10 7
♣ K 10 9 5

(Issie)
♠ A K Q
♡ Q 9
♢ K Q
♣ A Q J 8 7 6

East passed, and Issie opened 2 ♣, finally playing the hand in 6 NT. Aunt Agatha led the knave of spades, and Issie cashed his three top honours, East discarding the knave of hearts on the third round. Issie's first reaction was to try for the 3–3 club break (or the 10 9 falling in two rounds); but a further problem would arise if the queen of clubs was allowed to win. Should he continue the suit or not? Alternatively, if the defence won the second club lead with the king, a heart switch might prove disastrous. From Mildred's discard it looked as if she held the king of hearts, and if she also held the king of clubs Issie thought he could make his contract whatever the distribution in the minor suits.

'I'm going to trust you, Mildred,' said Issie, giving Jeremy a meaningful look. I was not quite sure whether he was preparing his alibi or making certain that Jeremy was following his brilliantly conceived plan. Anyway, he cashed the king and queen of diamonds and then entered dummy with the ace of hearts to cash the ace of diamonds and two spade winners. This was the position before the last spade was led:

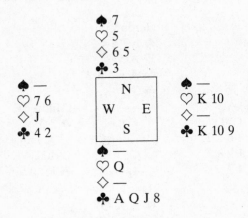

On the seven of spades East had to part with the ten of hearts in order to avoid setting up all the clubs, while Issie carefully discarded the eight of clubs. Now a successful club finesse was followed by the queen of hearts, and Mildred had no way of avoiding the final ignominy of leading into Issie's A Q of clubs.

Issie was very pleased with himself and kept looking at Jeremy for approval. Poor Mildred, on the other hand, was far from happy, as Aunt Agatha was inclined to blame her for that rather fatuous discard of the knave of hearts. True, it probably convinced Issie that the king of hearts really was with East, and once he had made that assumption it was an attractive line to play East for the king of clubs as well. There was always the additional bonus that if the diamonds were divided 3–3 he would have no hassle over the blockage and entry problem. When I could get a word in, I suggested that Issie had played with the odds, carefully omitting to mention whether those odds included or excluded the heart information. I only wish I could have filmed the various reactions. Mildred looked as though she could have kissed me. Issie, preening himself, muttered: 'Of course, of course.' Aunt Agatha frowned and looked at me suspiciously. She wasn't sure if I was pouring oil on troubled waters or whether I was really genuine. In any case she resented having her whipping-boy eased out of her reach. Jeremy gave me a cynical grin, which might have meant anything. Roughly interpreted, I suspect it said: 'Now pull the other one, it's got bells on it!'

THE LAST SAY

Slide-rule enthusiasts will no doubt have fun assessing the correct line of play without East's signalling extravaganza. All things being equal, the ace of clubs followed by the queen probably gives declarer his best chance. Apart from the 3–3 break, this play caters for the blank king of clubs and the doubleton 10 9. However, all things are far from being equal, since the second club forces dummy into making an uncomfortable discard. Without any evidence as to the location of the king of hearts, maybe the queen of clubs at trick four offers the best chance of success. One thing, however, stands out a mile: East's discard of the knave of hearts in the circumstances was asinine. If defenders wish to signal their high cards to each other, especially in slam contracts, they should remember that the enemy are tuned in to the same wavelength, so enthusiasm should be tempered with discretion.

The next hand of note was neatly played by Jeremy, and this time it was Aunt Agatha who received the treatment. Jeremy is now in the South seat. You might like to make your own plan before looking at the full deal. The bidding was simply 2 NT, 4 NT and finally 6 NT.

```
Game all              ♠ A J
Dealer South          ♡ A 7 2
                      ◇ 8 6 3 2
                      ♣ Q 10 3 2
                  ┌───────────┐
                  │     N     │
                  │  W     E  │
                  │     S     │
                  └───────────┘
                      ♠ K Q 10 9 3
                      ♡ K 5 4
                      ◇ A Q 4
                      ♣ A K
```

West, Aunt Agatha, led the eight of spades, and Jeremy cashed his winners in this suit. Aunt Agatha followed four times and then discarded the five of diamonds. Dummy parted with three diamonds while East, who had followed to two rounds of spades, discarded the three and eight of hearts and the four of clubs. On the ace and king of clubs everyone followed. What now?

It seemed improbable that the knave of clubs would come down but there was always the diamond finesse to fall back on. However, before committing himself to that chance Jeremy decided to try and obtain some more information. He cashed the king of hearts and entered dummy with the ace of hearts, West following with the six and the nine and East with the ten and the knave. On the queen of clubs East threw a diamond. At this point Jeremy reasoned that East must hold the queen of hearts (who would unguard the suit holding J 10 x x?) so it must be safe to throw West in with the knave of clubs to lead up to his A Q of diamonds.

This was the full hand:

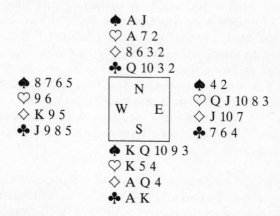

```
                    ♠ A J
                    ♡ A 7 2
                    ◇ 8 6 3 2
                    ♣ Q 10 3 2
  ♠ 8 7 6 5                          ♠ 4 2
  ♡ 9 6          ┌──────────┐        ♡ Q J 10 8 3
  ◇ K 9 5        │    N     │        ◇ J 10 7
  ♣ J 9 8 5      │ W     E  │        ♣ 7 6 4
                 │    S     │
                 └──────────┘
                    ♠ K Q 10 9 3
                    ♡ K 5 4
                    ◇ A Q 4
                    ♣ A K
```

Aunt Agatha had to admit defeat, but it was clear that she did not like being end-played any more than seeing her partner in that position. Grudgingly she conceded that Jeremy had handled the contract with reasonable efficiency, but she was somewhat caustic about Mildred's club discard. 'That small club was an idiotic chuck,' she admonished, somewhat unreasonably. 'Why not a small diamond, then he wouldn't have had a complete count?'

Poor Mildred, it just wasn't her day for discards, but Jeremy assured everyone that he would have made the contract in any case, which at least pleased one of his opponents and paved the way for the game to proceed.

THE LAST SAY

This time my sympathies are entirely with Mildred over that club
discard. Although one is naturally reluctant to discard from a suit
which may subsequently provide the enemy with a complete
count, or a strongly inferential one, there are greater
priorities—such as maintaining an adequate guard. Remember,
on the fifth spade Aunt Agatha shed a diamond, anxious not to
reveal too much information about the heart suit. If East also
discards a diamond, declarer can simply duck a diamond and still
get home by laying down the ace when he regains the lead.
Although Jeremy was no doubt trying to ease the tension when
he maintained that he would have made his contract regardless of
Mildred's discards, this is not the sort of hand that would ever
defeat him. Too many clues emerge and a first-class player soon
turns them to his advantage.

Jeremy played another hand which I really thought would cause
Aunt Agatha to fly into orbit. Had we been able to record her
inner turbulence on the Richter Scale . . . now that would have
been interesting.

E–W game +60
Dealer East

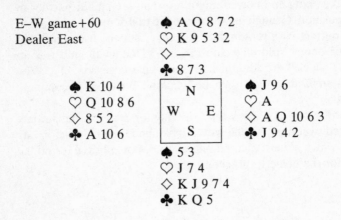

♠ A Q 8 7 2
♡ K 9 5 3 2
♢ —
♣ 8 7 3

♠ K 10 4
♡ Q 10 8 6
♢ 8 5 2
♣ A 10 6

♠ J 9 6
♡ A
♢ A Q 10 6 3
♣ J 9 4 2

♠ 5 3
♡ J 7 4
♢ K J 9 7 4
♣ K Q 5

The bidding:

S	W	N	E
(Jeremy)	(A. A.)	(Issie)	(Mildred)
—	—	—	1 ◇
No	1 NT	2 ◇	No
2 NT	Dble	3 ◇	Dble
3 ♡	Dble	No	No
No			

With sixty on score and a flat hand, Aunt Agatha decided that 1 NT was the most descriptive bid—and also gave her the best chance of playing the hand. For his part, Issie wanted to know if Jeremy had any fit for one of his majors. Having twisted Jeremy's arm, he found out, but the level was dangerously high and Aunt Agatha doubled as though she really meant it.

Aunt Agatha led the eight of diamonds, which East was allowed to win with the ace, dummy discarding a club. The club switch was won by Aunt Agatha's ace, and Jeremy took his first trick when Aunt Agatha returned a club. The spade finesse and spade ruff went smoothly enough. Furthermore, Jeremy was now reasonably certain that East must hold the blank ace of hearts. Nothing else made sense. So he ruffed his last club in dummy and led a low heart. East won, perforce, leaving this position:

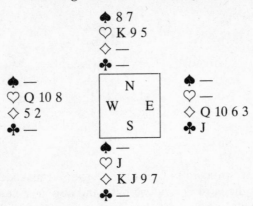

The defence have three tricks, declarer has five, and it is East to play. It really does not matter what the defence schemes up at this point as they cannot take more than one trick—providing declarer doesn't make a careless mistake. In fact East led the knave of clubs, Jeremy ruffed with the knave of hearts (he could also have discarded had he so wished) and Aunt Agatha overruffed with the queen. But dummy did not take this trick; instead, Jeremy underruffed! Well, that was the pretty way of doing it.

Now Aunt Agatha had a choice. She could play a trump, when dummy's hand would be high; or she could play a diamond round to Jeremy's K J and wait for the trumps to be trapped two tricks later. Aunt Agatha was not pleased. Had it been anyone else but a first-class player at the wheel, and a stranger to boot, I think everyone would have come in for a blasting. As it was, if looks could kill. . . .

Issie was thrilled with the result, but I think this was a form of narcissism. He had fallen in love with his own bidding rather than admiring Jeremy's dummy play.

THE LAST SAY

When the points are nearly evenly divided and the bidding becomes competitive it is only natural for the sparks to fly. A sizeable penalty, or a lucky make, is an outcome not entirely without precedent, so why Aunt Agatha should have got so worked up about this hand is beyond me. Maybe she thought she was going to teach Jeremy a sharp lesson and the disappointment was too great a burden to bear. The fact that Issie was somewhat under par for his bid seemed to go by unnoticed, or at any rate without comment, but to be fair it is the successful player that so often picks the right moment to make the wrong bid.

After a few more hands there was a new line-up. Aunt Agatha played with her favourite nephew against Jeremy and Mildred, while Issie was a very busy kibitzer.

It has to be admitted that Aunt Agatha really won some medals in this rubber—as she told us herself in no uncertain terms when it was all over. This was one of the early deals. It was love all and Aunt Agatha (South) became the declarer in 4 ♡ after the sequence 1 ♡, 3 ♡.

```
              ♠ 8 7 5 4
              ♡ K Q 6 5
              ◇ K J 9
              ♣ 10 4
          ┌───────────┐
          │     N     │
          │  W     E  │
          │     S     │
          └───────────┘
              ♠ K 10
              ♡ A 10 8 3
              ◇ A Q 6
              ♣ Q 9 7 2
```

Perhaps I pushed a bit in raising to 3 ♡ on the North hand. Clearly I am worth 2½ ♡, but with this aceless collection it might be prudent to adopt the more cautious approach. Still, had I bid only 2 ♡ there would have been no story to tell. Mildred (West) cashed the ace and king of clubs and ace of spades. Aunt Agatha won trick four with the king of spades, and then there was a pause as she considered the developments. How should she continue?

Aunt Agatha reasoned that not even Mildred would adopt such a kitchen-bridge defence as to cash all her aces and kings without a motive. And what could that motive be except that she expected to take a trump trick as well? Therefore, Mildred held four hearts to the knave! 'Of course,' said Aunt Agatha in an aside to me later, 'it was pretty naive of Mildred to play like that. She might have known it would arouse my suspicions.' I believe Aunt Agatha flatters her friend if she really thinks Mildred can divine her reactions. Anyway Mildred would probably say that Aunt Agatha is permanently suspicious, so there was nothing she could do to alter the norm.

This was the full deal:

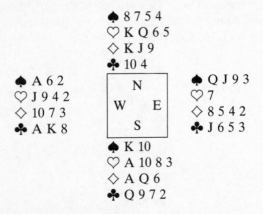

Although of course the natural play is a small heart to the king, catering for four to the knave with East, Aunt Agatha stuck to her guns and led the ace—noting with satisfaction the fall of the seven—and followed it with the ten. Mildred, looking as innocent as a baby, which doesn't present too many difficulties for her, made no attempt to cover the ten—and nor did dummy. The rest was plain sailing. A heart to dummy, a spade ruff and dummy re-entered with a top diamond to draw the last trump.

'Never thought you would make that contract,' exclaimed Issie unbelievingly. 'Fancy playing the hearts like that. It was really quite inspired.'

Mildred blinked and shook her head sadly. She couldn't believe it either but refrained from comment. Even Aunt Agatha was surprisingly silent at the end of the hand. Perhaps she enjoyed the air of mystery surrounding her play and was not prepared to destroy it—for the time being.

THE LAST SAY

Admittedly West had a slightly awkward play at trick three, but with a balanced hand showing in dummy there was no necessity to get so active. The fact that she defended with such aggression made Aunt Agatha look for a reason. Once the diagnosis was complete the treatment was almost routine. West fell into the common trap of directing her mind to one issue and ignoring everything else. Had she asked herself how South was going to get rid of any spade losers she happened to have, then she would not have cashed the ace of spades.

It seemed to me that Mildred was chesting her cards somewhat ostentatiously for the next few hands, but I might have been mistaken. Anyway, it wasn't long before Aunt Agatha was busy pulling off another coup.

Game all
Dealer South

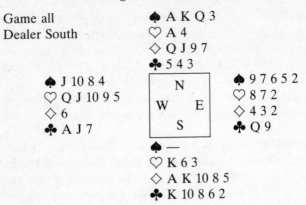

                    ♠ A K Q 3
                    ♡ A 4
                    ♢ Q J 9 7
                    ♣ 5 4 3

♠ J 10 8 4   ♠ 9 7 6 5 2
♡ Q J 10 9 5   N   ♡ 8 7 2
♢ 6   W   E   ♢ 4 3 2
♣ A J 7   S   ♣ Q 9

                    ♠ —
                    ♡ K 6 3
                    ♢ A K 10 8 5
                    ♣ K 10 8 6 2

This was the somewhat unusual bidding sequence:

S	W	N	E
(A. A.)	(Mildred)	(F. N.)	(Jeremy)
1 ♢	1 ♡	2 ♡	No
6 ♢!	No	No	No

Explaining her leap to 6 ♢ when the hand was over, Aunt
Agatha said that she knew I had diamonds with her and she
didn't want to give the opponents—especially Jeremy—any
gratuitous information.

The queen of hearts was led and won in dummy. Two rounds
of trumps were followed by the king of hearts and a heart ruff.
The last trump was drawn and a further round cashed to arrive
at the following position, South to play:

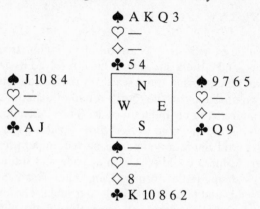

♠ A K Q 3
♡ —
◇ —
♣ 5 4

♠ J 10 8 4
♡ —
◇ —
♣ A J

♠ 9 7 6 5
♡ —
◇ —
♣ Q 9

♠ —
♡ —
◇ 8
♣ K 10 8 6 2

Aunt Agatha played the eight of diamonds and you can see Mildred's dilemma. Was she being squeezed in the black suits or could she afford to throw a spade? After an agonizing trance she discarded the knave of clubs, dummy threw the three of spades and Jeremy nearly upset his brandy glass. Aunt Agatha now led the two of clubs and lost to the ace, but the remainder of the tricks were hers.

'Why didn't you cash your spades when you were in dummy?' demanded Mildred, who had a nasty feeling that she had been conned despite Aunt Agatha's apparent carelessness in cutting herself off from her spade winners.

'Because then I would have had to play Jeremy for the ace of clubs and on your vulnerable overcall I was quite sure you held it,' replied Aunt Agatha.

There was a lot of chatter following this hand, and Issie seemed more excited in his role of kibitzer than if he'd been playing himself. He was certainly getting value for money. Only Jeremy was slightly subdued. I think he took the view that the situation was all too difficult for Mildred and therefore there was little point in pursuing it.

THE LAST SAY

Mildred was faced with an awkward problem but one that is not entirely new, and I think she should have resolved it. There is almost always a clue from the discards in these situations, and Jeremy's two of spades on the fourth round of diamonds stood out like a miniskirt in an Indian bazaar. Since he could surely afford that discard he held either three spades or five (he wouldn't discard from four and put his partner under pressure). If the latter, Mildred could part with a spade and still enjoy a good night's sleep. If the former, then Aunt Agatha held a doubleton spade and Mildred was in deep trouble. The knave of clubs would be best, since that still leaves the defence alive, but with Aunt Agatha at the wheel I don't think it would have been for long.

Forgetting the scientific side of it for a moment, but remembering that rather bizarre bidding sequence, it was surely more likely that Aunt Agatha held a shapely 0–3–5–5 than a mundane 2–3–5–3?

There were two more exciting hands from this memorable evening. In the first, Aunt Agatha again played quite magnificently.

Love all
Dealer South

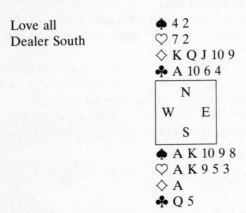

♠ 4 2
♡ 7 2
◇ K Q J 10 9
♣ A 10 6 4

```
      N
  W       E
      S
```

♠ A K 10 9 8
♡ A K 9 5 3
◇ A
♣ Q 5

The bidding:

S (A. A.)	W (Jeremy)	N (Issie)	E (Mildred)
2 ♣	No	3 ◇	No
3 ♡	No	4 ♣	No
4 NT	No	5 ◇	No
6 NT			

Jeremy led the three of clubs, and when dummy played low East produced the king. How should Aunt Agatha plan the play?

Annoyingly, for Aunt Agatha, Jeremy had found the only lead to create problems—assuming the spades are divided 3–3 or there is a singleton or doubleton honour. On any other lead the ace of diamonds and the two top spades are cashed and the rest is plain sailing.

This was the full hand:

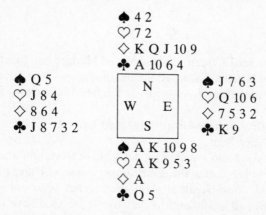

```
                 ♠ 4 2
                 ♡ 7 2
                 ◇ K Q J 10 9
                 ♣ A 10 6 4
   ♠ Q 5          ┌─────────┐     ♠ J 7 6 3
   ♡ J 8 4        │    N    │     ♡ Q 10 6
   ◇ 8 6 4        │ W     E │     ◇ 7 5 3 2
   ♣ J 8 7 3 2    │    S    │     ♣ K 9
                 └─────────┘
                 ♠ A K 10 9 8
                 ♡ A K 9 5 3
                 ◇ A
                 ♣ Q 5
```

Aunt Agatha's first move was to ditch the queen of clubs on the king, so as to make way for the finesse of the knave. Mildred studied this play with more than a little suspicion and after some thought switched to the seven of spades. Aunt Agatha won with the ace, and now a really critical decision had to be taken. Should she cash the king of spades or the ace and king of hearts before taking her minor-suit winners? Of course, the idea was either a double squeeze or a major-suit squeeze against East, but she had to guess the major-suit holdings correctly. After a short trance she cashed the king of spades and the red suit aces, and then took the club finesse. The ace of clubs and three rounds of diamonds followed to leave this position:

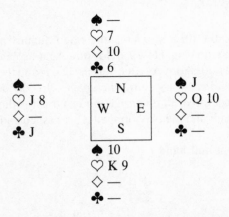

When the ten of diamonds was played Mildred had to let go a heart, Aunt Agatha discarded the ten of spades—it had done its duty—and now Jeremy was squeezed in hearts and clubs. Small slam made.

'Played the wrong way up,' observed Issie, being something of a result merchant.

'Well, if you hadn't made that dotty bid of four clubs and said something sensible, like three notrumps, *you* would have played it,' retorted Aunt Agatha. And then as an apparent after-thought: 'But all in all hands played by me are usually worth an extra trick or two so no doubt you were right to try and steer the contract my way.' I didn't dare look at Jeremy, but wondered what on earth he was thinking.

'Pity you didn't return my suit, partner,' said Jeremy, more to break the uneasy hush than as a constructive criticism.

'Oh, I couldn't do that,' replied Mildred, obviously surprised that Jeremy should introduce such a quaint idea. 'It would have given her a free finesse and I wasn't even sure that she had a second club. Besides, she did it herself later on.' I think Jeremy saw the futility of pressing the point because he said no more, but his line of thinking certainly wasn't lost on Aunt Agatha. Her silence alone confirmed that point.

THE LAST SAY

As the cards lay 6 ♠ would have succeeded, although perhaps a shade lucky; 6 NT was a fair contract until Jeremy so nearly upset the applecart with that awkward lead. And, of course, he was bang on target with his observation to Mildred. If she returns a club at trick two declarer must fail. The point is that the club continuation completely destroys the timing so that Aunt Agatha can't cash her spades before running the diamonds. The squeeze now becomes inoperative. As to Mildred's assertion that she couldn't be sure if declarer had a second club—the answer lies in Jeremy's lead. Assuming the three of clubs to be a true card, declarer had to have at least a doubleton, and from the play of the queen under the king it was a thousand pounds to a pinch of snuff that it was precisely a doubleton.

The following hand reflected a tremendous battle of wits between Aunt Agatha and Jeremy, but this time it was Jeremy who prevailed.

E–W game
Dealer West

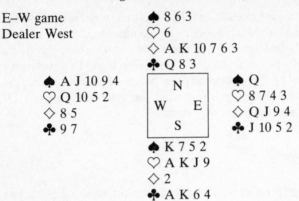

```
                ♠ 8 6 3
                ♡ 6
                ◇ A K 10 7 6 3
                ♣ Q 8 3
  ♠ A J 10 9 4       N        ♠ Q
  ♡ Q 10 5 2                  ♡ 8 7 4 3
  ◇ 8 5        W       E      ◇ Q J 9 4
  ♣ 9 7              S        ♣ J 10 5 2
                ♠ K 7 5 2
                ♡ A K J 9
                ◇ 2
                ♣ A K 6 4
```

The bidding:

S	W	N	E
(Jeremy)	(A. A.)	(Mildred)	(Issie)
—	No	No	No
1 ♣	No	1 ◇	No
1 ♡	No	2 ◇	No
2 NT	No	3 NT	No
No	No		

Aunt Agatha led the knave of spades, and Jeremy won this trick with the king. With chances abounding he saw no necessity to commit himself to any particular line prematurely, so he exited with a spade. Aunt Agatha could have cashed four tricks at this point, but she reasoned that if Jeremy was content for her to do that then it couldn't be in her best interests. This was good thinking, because Issie would not have relished finding too many discards (he threw a small heart at trick two). In practice Aunt Agatha switched to the eight of diamonds. Jeremy won in dummy and cashed a second diamond. Now three rounds of clubs ending in dummy revealed the 4–2 break, but the last fence was negotiated safely when he returned to his hand with the ace of hearts and once more exited with a spade.

It is West to play, the defence having taken just two tricks:

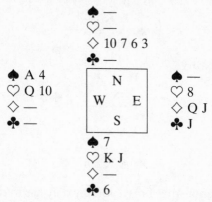

Aunt Agatha was able to cash her two spade winners, but she then had to concede the last two hearts to Jeremy.

'Why didn't you cash your spades at once and avoid the end-play?' enquired Issie, giving Aunt Agatha a hurt look. But, of course, he hadn't really considered the implications of his remark.

'How many do you suggest I should have cashed?' retorted Aunt Agatha in a voice that heralded a build-up of venom just aching to be released.

Suddenly realizing that several discards would have proved an embarrassment to him, Issie said: 'Of course, you can only cash three spades because I think four would squeeze me.' And then, warming to his theme: 'But that would get you off the hook. Jeremy couldn't end-play you and couldn't take the heart finesse to advantage. Furthermore, I should not be squeezed if I only have to find three discards.'

Jeremy looked as though he was about to say something, but you have to be quick if you want to get in in front of Aunt Agatha, and she had no intention of letting anyone else speak. 'Really, Issie, your analysis is terrible these days. First of all let's see what happens if I take all my spades. This would be the position after five tricks:

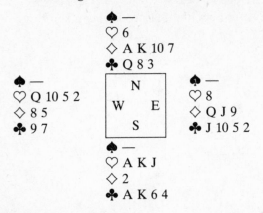

♠ —
♡ 6
◇ A K 10 7
♣ Q 8 3

♠ —   ♠ —
♡ Q 10 5 2   ♡ 8
◇ 8 5   ◇ Q J 9
♣ 9 7   ♣ J 10 5 2

♠ —
♡ A K J
◇ 2
♣ A K 6 4

'Now, no matter what I play, Jeremy only has to cash the ace and king of hearts and you, dear Issie, are squeezed into pulp. If we add a spade to my hand, and therefore one more card all round, Jeremy simply ducks a diamond to you when I switch. If by any chance I switch to a club, he wins in hand, cashes two top hearts and again ducks a diamond to you. Now I hope you are satisfied,' concluded Aunt Agatha, indicating that in any case the discussion was over and it was time for everyone to get on with the next hand.

THE LAST SAY

Preposterous as it may seem at first blush, Issie might have engineered a fine result for his side had he doubled 3 NT. With only six points many players would regard such a suggestion as eccentric, if not actually obscene, but the fact remains that there is quite a lot going for the double. Both North and South have limited their hands, so there is not likely to be much to spare. Furthermore, the cards are known to be lying well for the defence, with all the suits breaking poorly. Finally, the double would suggest a diamond lead, which would perhaps avoid giving declarer an unnecessary present with the opening gambit. With nowhere obvious to go for tricks, declarer would probably duck the diamond to East, who would switch to the queen of spades. South must hold off, otherwise he is down at once, and now East will switch to a heart. Perhaps West will be allowed to win this trick, in which case she must return the nine of clubs. Now the defence can simply sit back and wait for their last two tricks. Paradoxically the double becomes successful because East is not overburdened with top cards.

Oh yes, there were more ups and downs before we could decently take our leave, but they will have to be related on another occasion. Maybe the whole evening was summed up by Jeremy when he quietly observed: 'After tonight the trials at the weekend will seem quite peaceful.'

4. Christmas with Aunt Agatha

Christmas with Aunt Agatha invariably involves one in bridge. Maybe it is not always of the highest quality, but somehow the hands seem to enter into the spirit of the occasion.

I remember one year when the outside world mirrored all the romantic conceptions of the festive season. Deep layers of pure white snow, trees glistening in the sunlight and an aura of bonhomie which even pervaded Aunt Agatha's home. Despite the traditional setting, the cards seemed to behave strangely—or was it the players, affected by Aunt Agatha's ample hospitality? I leave you to judge.

Game all
Dealer South

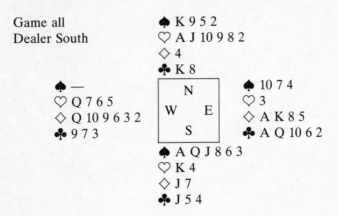

North
♠ K 9 5 2
♡ A J 10 9 8 2
♢ 4
♣ K 8

West
♠ —
♡ Q 7 6 5
♢ Q 10 9 6 3 2
♣ 9 7 3

East
♠ 10 7 4
♡ 3
♢ A K 8 5
♣ A Q 10 6 2

South
♠ A Q J 8 6 3
♡ K 4
♢ J 7
♣ J 5 4

The bidding:

S	W	N	E
(Issie)	(Mildred)	(Sally)	(A. A.)
1 ♠	No	2 ♡	Dble
2 ♠	3 ♢	4 ♠	5 ♢
No	No	5 ♡	No
5 ♠	No	No	No

Considering the Christmas celebrations the auction was remarkably accurate, although I am not in love with Sally's 'twice round the gasworks' bid of 2 ♡. A direct jump to 4 ♠ would be much better. As you can see, Mildred can make 5 ♢, while Issie has plenty of problems in 5 ♠. But thereby hangs the tale.

Mildred led the ten of diamonds, Aunt Agatha winning with the king and Issie playing the knave. Although Mildred made what she considered to be the 'book' lead, it had the effect of concealing the actual number of cards held in the suit. Thus from Aunt Agatha's point of view the knave could be singleton. Reluctant to concede a possible ruff and discard, Aunt Agatha now played the three of hearts, saying, 'There you are, Issie dear—your Christmas present.'

Making the most of his present, or so he thought at the time, Issie played low from his own hand, while Mildred, with an agonized look at everybody in turn, fingered first the queen and then the five. Had she settled for the queen that would have been the end of the story, but in fact it was the five of hearts that appeared on the table. Issie gobbled up this trick with dummy's eight and played on trumps. However, when they broke 3–0 there was no way in which he could bring in the heart suit for all his discards, or indeed avoid two more losers.

Aunt Agatha was tickled pink with her play of the three of hearts, quite forgetting in the excitement of the moment that a second diamond would have totally eclipsed the dummy. As it was, the heart switch ran two great risks: (1) that Issie would do the right thing; and (2) that Mildred would do the wrong thing. Unattractive sort of odds—even at Christmas. To be fair to Aunt Agatha though, she had her problems. Perhaps in more sombre—or sober—moments a strong case could be made for leading a second diamond.

Of course, had Issie rejected Aunt Agatha's little gift and won with his king of hearts he could have drawn trumps, taken the heart finesse and made the remainder of the tricks.

'Should have known better,' moaned Issie. Then with a wry grin: 'Isn't there a well-known saying, "Beware of Greek gifts and Christmas presents from Aunt Agatha"?'

THE LAST SAY

The dangers of painting a pretty picture are well illustrated here, for it is doubtful if even the redoubtable Aunt Agatha would have ventured a move over a direct response of 4 ♠. North's hand is not powerful in top cards and for the odd occasion that a slam is missed many game contracts will sail home unmolested after wholesale tactics. It is worth reflecting that it is North–South who need to save against East–West, despite the fact that the former hold the balance of the points. As to the play, only dummy comes out of it completely blameless (she did her bit in the bidding). Mildred's lead of the ten of diamonds was fatuous. It should have been obvious from the auction that the intermediate diamonds would have no significance in play. Therefore if Mildred wanted to lead a diamond, the fourth highest, to help her partner with the count, or the queen, hoping to retain the lead so that she could decide what to do having seen the dummy, suggest themselves as much better bets than the ten. But best of all must surely be a club, so obvious when you consider the bidding. Although Mildred failed in her nursing duties, Aunt Agatha was not as perceptive as usual. The three of hearts was a dangerous play, and since it was unlikely that Mildred had a seven-card suit the diamond return stood out.

Given his Christmas present, Issie promptly eschewed the recognized code of etiquette and handed it back again.

It takes a great deal to subdue Issie for long, and he soon recovered his ebullient confidence when this hand occurred a few deals later.

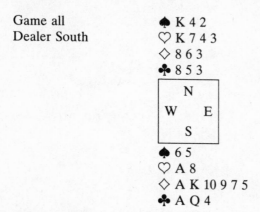

Game all
Dealer South

♠ K 4 2
♡ K 7 4 3
◇ 8 6 3
♣ 8 5 3

N
W   E
S

♠ 6 5
♡ A 8
◇ A K 10 9 7 5
♣ A Q 4

The bidding:

S	W	N	E
(Issie)	(Mildred)	(Sally)	(A. A.)
1 ◇	No	1 ♡	2 ♣
3 NT	No	No	No

If Issie's jump to 3 NT strikes you as being too optimistic, remember it was Christmas. After some thought Mildred led the queen of spades. How should Issie plan the play?

If you decide to duck, Aunt Agatha will play the eight and Mildred will continue with the knave. If you duck again Aunt Agatha will play the three, win the third round with the ace and switch to the knave of clubs. You put in the queen, which holds the trick. What now?

Suppose you play a heart to dummy's king and lead a diamond. Aunt Agatha follows with the queen. How do you proceed?

In fact the play followed the pattern described, and Issie, without the slightest hesitation, allowed Aunt Agatha's queen of diamonds to hold the trick. Shortly afterwards he was able to spread his cards and claim nine tricks, for game and rubber. This was the full deal:

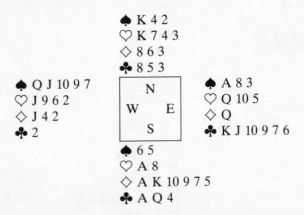

```
                 ♠ K 4 2
                 ♡ K 7 4 3
                 ◇ 8 6 3
                 ♣ 8 5 3
  ♠ Q J 10 9 7        N         ♠ A 8 3
  ♡ J 9 6 2                     ♡ Q 10 5
  ◇ J 4 2        W       E      ◇ Q
  ♣ 2                S          ♣ K J 10 9 7 6
                 ♠ 6 5
                 ♡ A 8
                 ◇ A K 10 9 7 5
                 ♣ A Q 4
```

Issie was very pleased with himself and Sally made all the right sort of noises in encouragement. 'Pays to take a chance when you know where all the cards are,' gloated Issie.

'Would I have done better to have led a club?' enquired Mildred, obviously looking for praise rather than a considered appraisal of her choice. Aunt Agatha just glared—a festive glare, mind you, less piercing than usual. And then, breaking the silence occasioned by her expression: 'Of course, Issie is just too incredibly lucky. He shoots 3 NT and then finds not only dummy with the right cards but his opponents as well.'

THE LAST SAY

It is interesting to consider if there is a better rebid on the South hand after East has intervened with 2 ♣. While 3 NT may savour of one gin too many, anything less might well be labelled 'lacking in spirit'. With every possibility of getting a club lead 3 NT looks a fair speculation, but it is when you come to consider an alternative choice that the bid chosen suddenly becomes obvious. For example, 3 ♢, clearly an underbid, throws too much emphasis on the diamond suit and leaves partner in the air over the club guard. I suppose 2 NT is some sort of solution, but it imposes an unnecessary burden on partner's shoulders, and is also something of an underbid.

Issie handled the play beautifully. Having taken the right view of the spades he carefully entered dummy with a heart so that he could play a diamond towards his own hand. When Aunt Agatha produced the queen of diamonds he correctly allowed her to hold the trick, virtually guaranteeing success apart from a very unlikely layout in the red suits. Aunt Agatha, however, was not completely foot perfect. She would have done much better to play a heart at trick four, not a club. This would have tested Issie right to the top of the Christmas tree. He can still make his contract providing he wins in dummy, takes the club finesse and then plays a low diamond. Not quite so easy, and hardly a textbook approach.

The line-up for the next rubber was much the same as before, except that Aunt Agatha and Mildred exchanged places. It was as a result of the next two deals that my aunt made a somewhat un-Christmas-like declaration. 'Run-of-the-mill players should be issued with a handyman's kit: a pocket computer, an abacus and a list of their favourite slogans. Then, with a bit of luck, they would never have to think at all.' This caustic outburst was occasioned not so much by partner's mishaps in defence as by the inane explanations that followed the disasters.

The problem on the first hand is one that occurs frequently.

Love all   (Sally)
Dealer South   ♠ K 10 5 3
                            ♡ Q 8 3
                            ◇ Q 5 2
                            ♣ K 5 4

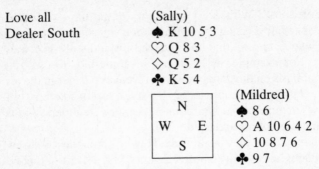

                                        (Mildred)
                                        ♠ 8 6
                                        ♡ A 10 6 4 2
                                        ◇ 10 8 7 6
                                        ♣ 9 7

The bidding had been uninformative. Issie (South) opened 1 ♠
and when Sally raised him to 2 ♠ he continued to 4 ♠. Aunt
Agatha led the seven of hearts, dummy played low and
Mildred . . .?

This was the full deal:

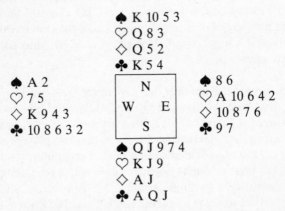

In her wisdom, Mildred won with the ace of hearts and from
that moment onwards there was no defence. Aunt Agatha had
found the only attack to defeat the contract but, of course, it
necessitated Mildred's co-operation by ducking the first round to
preserve communications. Obviously Aunt Agatha's lead might
have been a singleton, in which case Mildred would have been
correct to take her ace at once. Rather needlessly, perhaps, Aunt

Agatha demanded to know why Mildred had not refused the first heart. 'Oh, I had to take the trick,' Mildred replied, 'you might have had a singleton. Besides, third player plays high, you know, and one shouldn't finesse against partner.' No doubt Mildred could have trotted out a few more things we all learned at our mothers' knees, but the look on Aunt Agatha's face was enough to silence her. In fact it was enough to silence anybody.

THE LAST SAY

There is no denying that 3 NT is iron-clad against any defence—something that was missed in the post-mortem. When striking a major-suit fit it is never easy to change to notrumps (a sort of Stayman in reverse), but had Issie rebid 3 NT, instead of 4 ♠, Sally would have been happy to pass.

One cannot give a foolproof remedy for Mildred's dilemma, but assuming no quick entry and no obvious inference that partner's lead must be a singleton, perhaps as good a guide as any is to base your decision on the shape of the two known hands. If singletons abound—play partner for one, too. If there are no singletons in sight—assume partner's hand falls into line and play him for a doubleton. Of course, if the trump suit looks solid you will have to play partner for a singleton regardless of any symmetrical considerations.

Although the next hand once more cast Mildred in the role of villain of the piece, I wonder how many of us would have done better.

N–S game
Dealer East

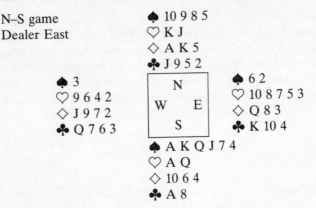

♠ 10 9 8 5
♡ K J
◇ A K 5
♣ J 9 5 2

♠ 3
♡ 9 6 4 2
◇ J 9 7 2
♣ Q 7 6 3

♠ 6 2
♡ 10 8 7 5 3
◇ Q 8 3
♣ K 10 4

♠ A K Q J 7 4
♡ A Q
◇ 10 6 4
♣ A 8

The bidding:

S (Issie)	W (A. A.)	N (Sally)	E (Mildred)
—	—	—	No
2 ♠	No	3 ♠	No
4 ♣	No	4 ◇	No
4 ♡	No	5 ◇	No
6 ♠	No	No	No

A minute rearrangement of the red suits in dummy and thirteen tricks would be cold. As it was, even the small slam presented problems.

Aunt Agatha led the two of hearts. Issie won in hand and played the ace and a small spade, followed by the two of clubs from dummy. On the club trick East contributed the four, South the eight and West the queen. Declarer won the heart return, cashed the ace of clubs, entered dummy with the ace of diamonds and ruffed a club. When Mildred's king of clubs fell, Issie spread his cards and claimed the remainder of the tricks.

'Can't do anything about it, can we?' enquired Mildred somewhat apprehensively.

Aunt Agatha did not answer at once because the light had not yet dawned. But then, as the mist cleared away, her eyes narrowed and she fixed Mildred with a frosty glare. 'Of course we can beat it, if you have the wit to put in your ten of clubs when he plays the two from dummy.'

'But . . .' began Mildred.

'I know, I know,' interrupted Aunt Agatha, 'second player plays low!'

Issie is one of those players who assumes luck will be on his side. If the cards are recalcitrant, then he expects the defence to come to his rescue. If the defence are playing a fine game, then he expects the cards to lie well. The philosophy of an egotist, no doubt, but such thinking seems to enjoy a high ratio of success.

THE LAST SAY

Issie and Sally suffered the dreaded duplication when ten points are worth just two tricks. Even the best of players often fail to avoid this sort of trap. As to Mildred's failure to play the ten of clubs at trick four, it was hard to visualize that this defence would be so critical unless fully conversant with the situation. The key is that East holds three cards only in clubs, and therefore her king can be ruffed out if South can force West's queen with the eight. Furthermore, the ten can hardly cost when West has three or four cards in the suit.

Much to Aunt Agatha's disgust, Issie was still carrying all before him.

N–S game
Dealer East

♠ —
♡ A Q 7 5 2
◇ Q 5 3 2
♣ A Q 9 4

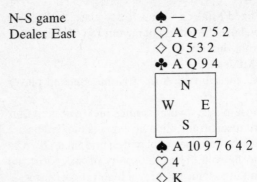

♠ A 10 9 7 6 4 2
♡ 4
◇ K
♣ J 10 7 3

The bidding:

S	W	N	E
(Issie)	(A. A.)	(Sally)	(Mildred)
—	—	—	No
No	3 ◇	3 ♡	No
4 ♠	No	No	Dble
No	No	No	

Feeling that he had no good vulnerable bid, Issie passed on the first round. Aunt Agatha, fearing the worst after Mildred's pass, tried to throw a spanner in the works with her pre-emptive effort in diamonds. This made life difficult for Sally, but she decided on a bold policy despite the flimsy heart suit — immediately to be regretted when the irrepressible Issie launched forth into 4 ♠. Mildred's double only confirmed Sally's misgivings.

Aunt Agatha led the ace of diamonds and switched to the three of hearts. Issie won with the ace and ruffed a heart, East playing the nine followed by the knave while West followed with the six. On the ace of spades Aunt Agatha played the knave and Mildred the three. How should South continue?

Here is the full hand:

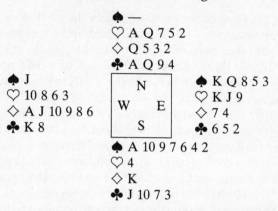

♠ —
♡ A Q 7 5 2
♢ Q 5 3 2
♣ A Q 9 4

♠ J
♡ 10 8 6 3
♢ A J 10 9 8 6
♣ K 8

♠ K Q 8 5 3
♡ K J 9
♢ 7 4
♣ 6 5 2

♠ A 10 9 7 6 4 2
♡ 4
♢ K
♣ J 10 7 3

Issie gave quite a lot of thought to his play at trick five. It looked as though East held five spades headed by the king, queen; also the king, knave, nine of hearts. Therefore, the king of clubs was surely right. Alternatively, if East held the king of clubs then West must hold a second spade honour otherwise East would have had an opening bid. Having made a pretty shrewd analysis, Issie led the knave of clubs, covered by the king and ace. A heart ruff felled Mildred's king and a second club to dummy enabled Issie to cash the queen of diamonds. This was the position with the defence having taken just one trick:

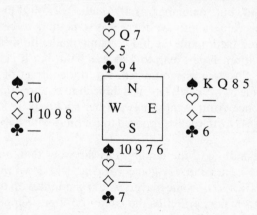

♠ —
♡ Q 7
♢ 5
♣ 9 4

♠ —
♡ 10
♢ J 10 9 8
♣ —

♠ K Q 8 5
♡ —
♢ —
♣ 6

♠ 10 9 7 6
♡ —
♢ —
♣ 7

Having unblocked the clubs —he threw the ten of clubs on the queen of diamonds —Issie could safely play the nine from dummy, but the queen of hearts, the card he chose, was just as good. Mildred threw the six of clubs (ruffing would not have helped) and Issie the seven. On the next card from dummy, East's minor spade pips were smothered by South.

Both Issie and Sally were overjoyed that everything had worked out so well and were quite voluble about their success. The fact that Mildred kept claiming that it should have been impossible with her trump holding only made her opponents more excited. It was left to Aunt Agatha to bring Issie and his partner down to earth as she observed: 'I don't know what you two are chortling about. You finish in a dotty contract, make it because you have the luck of Old Nick, and all the time 5 ♣ is as cold as ice.'

THE LAST SAY

The bidding savours strongly of Christmas. In the ordinary way Aunt Agatha's pre-empt of 3 ♢ would be an extremely doubtful contender. With a four-card major on the side and only six diamonds most experts would be reluctant to embark on a barrage bid, but remember Aunt Agatha was third-in-hand at favourable vulnerability, so there was something to be said for enterprising tactics and the bid certainly made life difficult for the opposition. Issie's leap to 4 ♠ was bold, but it gets better the more closely it is scrutinized. As to a contract of 5 ♣—a dream game as the cards lie—it is difficult to see how this can be reached once Aunt Agatha has put her spoke in. If Issie bids only 3 ♠, is North really supposed to continue with 4 ♣? Surely not.

Issie's handling of the dummy was shrewder than one might appreciate from a cursory glance. Having laid down the ace of spades at trick four, some players would continue with the ten of spades—to make certain of the trump position. Suppose Issie does this. East wins and returns a diamond. A second heart ruff followed by three rounds of clubs would leave dummy on play in this three-card ending:

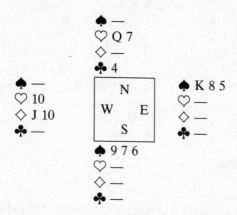

Whatever dummy plays, East ruffs low. Declarer overruffs but must then concede the last two tricks to East. One down.

With success following success there was no holding Issie, although he seemed to take a bit of a liberty on the following hand.

N–S game
Dealer North

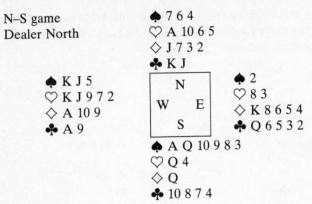

♠ 7 6 4
♡ A 10 6 5
♢ J 7 3 2
♣ K J

♠ K J 5
♡ K J 9 7 2
♢ A 10 9
♣ A 9

♠ 2
♡ 8 3
♢ K 8 6 5 4
♣ Q 6 5 3 2

♠ A Q 10 9 8 3
♡ Q 4
♢ Q
♣ 10 8 7 4

The bidding:

S (Issie)	W (A. A.)	N (Sally)	E (Mildred)
—	—	No	No
1 ♠	Dble	Rdble	2 ♢
No	No	2 ♠	3 ♣
No	3 ♢	Dble	No
3 ♠	Dble	No	No
No			

Issie was certainly not overburdened with the good things of life for his vulnerable opening. Ten points, including a bare queen, is flimsy material with which to initiate the attack—even at Christmas.

When Aunt Agatha kicked off with the ace and another club it appeared that there were five inescapable losers: two spades, and one trick in each of the other suits. However, Issie won the second trick in dummy and played the two of diamonds, his queen falling to Aunt Agatha's ace. Aunt Agatha could do no better than exit with the ten of diamonds which was ruffed by declarer. A club was now led towards the dummy, Aunt Agatha ruffing with the knave of spades and playing her final diamond.

But Issie had the matter well under control as he ruffed this trick, cashed the ace of spades and led his last club. This was the position before the ten of clubs was played, the defence having won three tricks:

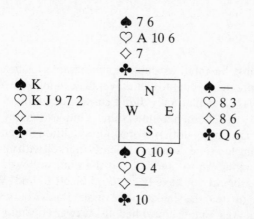

```
                    ♠ 7 6
                    ♡ A 10 6
                    ◇ 7
                    ♣ —
    ♠ K                         ♠ —
    ♡ K J 9 7 2    N            ♡ 8 3
    ◇ —          W   E          ◇ 8 6
    ♣ —            S            ♣ Q 6
                    ♠ Q 10 9
                    ♡ Q 4
                    ◇ —
                    ♣ 10
```

Not wanting to be on play, Aunt Agatha discarded a heart on the ten of clubs while dummy ruffed. However, the evil hour was only being postponed as Issie led dummy's seven of diamonds and ruffed. Again Aunt Agatha threw a heart, but now the ten of spades forced her to take the lead, and the heart return gave Issie the remainder of the tricks.

'I hoped he hadn't got the queen of hearts,' said Aunt Agatha unrealistically, as she watched Issie totting up the score. And then, as the thought suddenly struck her: 'Mildred, why on earth didn't you go up with your king of diamonds at trick three and lead a heart?'

As we have seen, Mildred has been reared in the traditions of 'second player plays low, third player plays high', and she was somewhat put out by Aunt Agatha's outrageous suggestion.

'But I thought . . .' began Mildred.

'That was the trouble,' interrupted Aunt Agatha, 'you didn't think, otherwise you would have realized that it could not cost a thing to play your king of diamonds. I knew Issie was bidding on seaweed, as usual. Vulnerable on ten points, including a bare queen, if you please.'

'Never underestimate the value of a bare woman,' said Issie. 'They're not all wanton hussies, you know!'

THE LAST SAY

Issie's bid must be rated as dubious, vulnerable against non-vulnerable opponents, but most of us would go along with it third in hand. It was clear that Sally didn't suspect anything, for she showed plenty of fight on her nine points. Unquestionably Aunt Agatha was right in her criticism of Mildred, although I am sure she was wasting her time. South was clearly marked with no more than one diamond on the bidding, so the king, followed by a heart switch, should not have been too difficult to find. Was it likely that South held the singleton ace of diamonds? I think not, because Aunt Agatha must have had an awkward opening lead, judging by her choice of the ace of clubs. No good player likes to catch thin air by leading an unsupported ace unless there is a good reason, or the alternative is even less attractive. With ◇ Q 10 9 the diamond lead would appear automatic.

Having left the scene of action for a walk in the snow, I returned hoping that I hadn't missed too many gems. That it had all been happening was only too obvious as Issie, who was temporarily on his own, looked as glum as a duck on a dry pond. A thousand pounds to a pinch of snuff, I thought, the fortunes have changed and Issie has been knocked for six. 'Cheer up,' I said consolingly, 'you look as though you've just received some devastating news. I know—your mother-in-law has been sacked from her job as chief test pilot at the broom factory and is coming to stay with you.'

'Don't be ridiculous,' retorted Issie, the ghost of a smile emerging at last. 'It's your Aunt Agatha. She's so infernally lucky. Her partners put her into impossible contracts—or she just gets there by herself—and then the miracles start to happen. One after the other. I tell you, she leads a charmed life. Just look at this.'

Love all
Dealer West

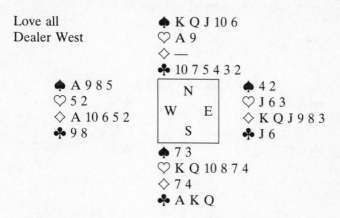

Love all
Dealer West

♠ K Q J 10 6
♡ A 9
♢ —
♣ 10 7 5 4 3 2

♠ A 9 8 5
♡ 5 2
♢ A 10 6 5 2
♣ 9 8

♠ 4 2
♡ J 6 3
♢ K Q J 9 8 3
♣ J 6

♠ 7 3
♡ K Q 10 8 7 4
♢ 7 4
♣ A K Q

The bidding:

S	W	N	E
(A. A.)	(Issie)	(Sally)	(Mildred)
—	No	No	3 ♢
3 ♡	5 ♢	6 ♡	No
No	No		

It seems that Issie didn't think there was much point in leading a diamond, so he chose the ace of spades. Mildred started a peter with the four, and Issie realized that he would have to continue the suit. Aunt Agatha won in dummy and now had to make an important decision. Who was more likely to hold three hearts—assuming a 3–2 break—East or West? Despite East's pre-empt it was West who had got really active in the bidding, jumping to five diamonds, clearly without too much in high cards. So, with West marked with four spades and length in diamonds, Aunt Agatha decided that it was East who was more likely to have three hearts. This meant that she, too, must continue spades. Mildred ruffed the third round, and declarer overruffed. Dummy was re-entered with the ace of hearts to lead a fourth spade. Mildred ruffed with her last trump, the knave, and Aunt Agatha overtrumped to leave this position:

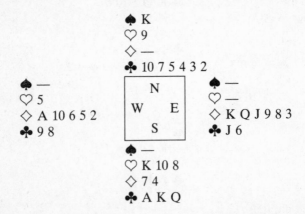

Now Aunt Agatha cashed two top clubs, played the eight of hearts to dummy's nine and then led the king of spades on which she pitched the master club! The club suit was now unblocked, and dummy was high.

THE LAST SAY

Sally showed tremendous imagination in the bidding—perhaps too much—while Issie's choice of lead might be registered on the birth certificate as Fatal Choice by Unlucky out of Aggression. A diamond, partner's suit, which perhaps is not so obvious with five of them, would have cooked Aunt Agatha's goose, no matter how much she had wriggled. In fact, any card other than the ace of spades would have presented Aunt Agatha with insoluble problems.

I suppose Mildred might have given Aunt Agatha the chance of going wrong had she refrained from ruffing the fourth round of spades, throwing a club instead. Aunt Agatha would have discarded a diamond, played a club to her hand and ruffed her last diamond. This would have been the position with dummy to play:

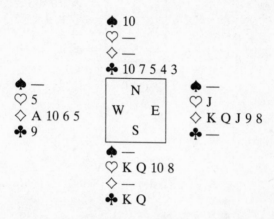

♠ 10
♡ —
◇ —
♣ 10 7 5 4 3

♠ —
♡ 5
◇ A 10 6 5
♣ 9

N
W   E
S

♠ —
♡ J
◇ K Q J 9 8
♣ —

♠ —
♡ K Q 10 8
◇ —
♣ K Q

Aunt Agatha's problem now is how to return to hand. She might have construed Mildred's failure to ruff as being consistent with holding only two trumps after all, in which case it would be essential to play a club. That would have been a hot defence by Mildred and I can't help feeling Aunt Agatha would have failed the test.

'It was unbearable,' moaned Issie, more to himself than to me.

I murmured something about Aunt Agatha having made the best of things after a lucky lead, but Issie wasn't listening. He was busy writing out this hand:

Christmas with Aunt Agatha

Game all
Dealer South

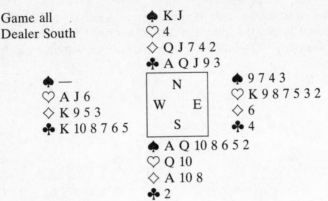

```
                      ♠ K J
                      ♡ 4
                      ◇ Q J 7 4 2
                      ♣ A Q J 9 3
        ♠ —              N           ♠ 9 7 4 3
        ♡ A J 6                      ♡ K 9 8 7 5 3 2
        ◇ K 9 5 3    W       E       ◇ 6
        ♣ K 10 8 7 6 5    S          ♣ 4
                      ♠ A Q 10 8 6 5 2
                      ♡ Q 10
                      ◇ A 10 8
                      ♣ 2
```

The bidding:

S	W	N	E
(A. A.)	(Issie)	(Sally)	(Mildred)
1 ♠	No	2 ◇	No
4 ♣	No	5 ♣	No
5 ◇	No	5 ♡	Dble
6 ◇	Dble	6 ♠	No
No	Dble	No	No
No			

From Issie's comments I gather he doubled the final contract more out of frustration than for any logical reason, but when he saw dummy his hopes rose. He led the ace of hearts and, as he put it, 'for lack of anything better to do', continued the suit. Superficially the minors appeared unattractive, and it was always possible that East might hold four spades to the ten, in which case ruffing in dummy would prove an embarrassment.

In practice, Aunt Agatha was far from embarrassed. She ruffed the heart in dummy, cashed the king of spades and played the queen of diamonds. The bidding seemed to indicate that West had the minor-suit kings, so when East failed to cover the diamond she overtook with her ace and ran five top spades to reach this position:

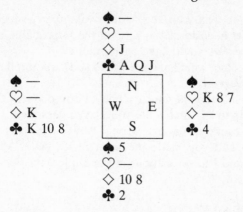

♠ —
♡ —
◊ J
♣ A Q J

♠ —   ♠ —
♡ —   ♡ K 8 7
◊ K   ◊ —
♣ K 10 8   ♣ 4

♠ 5
♡ —
◊ 10 8
♣ 2

When the five of spades was played, Issie was squeezed. He delayed the issue for a moment or so by throwing the eight of clubs, but Aunt Agatha made no mistake. She threw the knave of diamonds from dummy and took the club finesse for the remainder of the tricks.

'Wasn't that incredibly lucky?' demanded Issie.

At that very moment Aunt Agatha came back into the room and, hearing Issie's question, glanced at the hands on the table. 'Talking about me, I suppose,' she remarked. 'What you forget, Issie my dear, is that a player makes the most of his, or her, own good fortune. Take Sally, for example. She bid both the hands you are talking about to the hilt, but of course she was only exploiting her own good luck.'

'How do you mean, *her* good luck? What good luck did Sally have?' enquired Issie suspiciously.

He should have known Aunt Agatha better. With a mischievous smile she replied: 'Well, she had me as a partner and you, Issie dear, on lead. You can't get much luckier than that, can you?'

'But I ...' began Issie. 'No doubt,' interrupted Aunt Agatha, 'no doubt at all you were doing your best. But on the first hand that ace of spades was a real killer of a lead—for your side. And on the second, why didn't you switch to a club at trick two? That would have broken up all possibility of a squeeze, and I would have been forced to rely on the improbable diamond finesse. Now *that* would have been unlucky.'

'Well, Freddie, what have you got to add?' enquired my aunt, almost belligerently.

'You haven't left me much scope,' I complained, 'but it is probably fair to say that while you played very well, Issie was penalized severely for his wrong views. He was a little unfortunate and you made the most of it.' After all, it was Christmas, and I have relations in the Diplomatic Service.

THE LAST SAY

One point that was ignored in the post-mortem was Issie's highly questionable double of 6 ◇. Had he passed, Sally might well have done likewise. After all, the sequence 1 ♠, 2 ◇, 4 ♠ inferentially suggests a diamond fit (otherwise why not open 4 ♠?), and in fact Aunt Agatha had bid diamonds twice. Even against a slack defence declarer has no chance in the diamond slam.

As to West's play at trick two (against 6 ♠), a club switch has much more to commend it than one might think. With most distributions, even a free finesse (South has a club void) will be of no use to declarer. Only when declarer has three hearts and a club void plus spades solid down to the nine will the club switch prove disastrous. Against that is the dire necessity to play a club when the cards are distributed as in the diagram. For then, and only then, will the vital link for the squeeze be severed.

The part-score element at rubber bridge introduces many problems that are unfamiliar to tournament players. This was a hand I found quite fascinating.

Love all
E–W+60
Dealer West

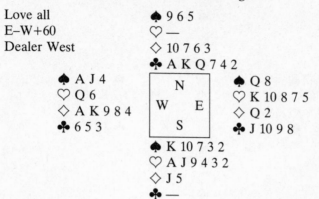

♠ 9 6 5
♡ —
♢ 10 7 6 3
♣ A K Q 7 4 2

♠ A J 4
♡ Q 6
♢ A K 9 8 4
♣ 6 5 3

♠ Q 8
♡ K 10 8 7 5
♢ Q 2
♣ J 10 9 8

♠ K 10 7 3 2
♡ A J 9 4 3 2
♢ J 5
♣ —

The bidding:

S (A. A.)	W (Issie)	N (Sally)	E (Mildred)
—	1 NT	2 ♣	2 ♡
No	No	3 ♣	Dble
3 ♠	Dble	No	No
No			

Aunt Agatha's pass over 2 ♡ was shrewder than it appears at
first blush. If, for example, you think she should have doubled,
just try the defence and see how you make out. Perhaps the best
lead is the knave of diamonds. East wins and plays the queen of
spades to the king and ace. The knave of spades and a spade ruff
follow. Now a heart to the queen (South must duck) and two top
diamonds permit South to ruff. At this point East has six tricks
and South one. This is the position:

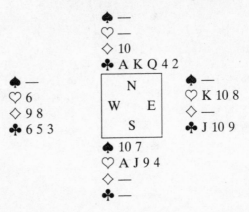

♠ —
♡ —
♢ 10
♣ A K Q 4 2

♠ —   ♠ —
♡ 6   ♡ K 10 8
♢ 9 8   ♢ —
♣ 6 5 3   ♣ J 10 9

♠ 10 7
♡ A J 9 4
♢ —
♣ —

South is on lead, and there is no way she can avoid allowing East to make two more tricks. Suppose she plays a spade. East ruffs and calmly plays clubs until such time as South end-plays herself by ruffing one of North's winners. A trump switch proves equally abortive.

'Ah,' you may say, 'but why didn't she bid two spades? After all, she knew that Sally must be void in hearts and therefore probably had a few spades.' True, that would seem a reasonable argument, but perhaps she thought that 2 ♡ undoubled would be sure to fail, so the substance was preferable to the shadow; or perhaps she was hoping for bigger things. Unravelling the workings of my aunt's mind is something I have long since decided is beyond me, rather like trying to pick the first three in correct order in a competitive handicap. Asked to speculate, I might place about 10 pence on the possibility that she had noted a gleam in Sally's eye which suggested that the bidding was not yet over and that bigger and better fish were swimming towards her net.

Anyway, let's return to Aunt Agatha's contract of 3 ♠ doubled. Issie led the ace of diamonds, dummy played the three, Mildred the two and Aunt Agatha the five. Forget the two concealed hands for a moment and try to work out what Issie should play at trick two. Have you decided?

In practice Issie switched to the four of spades, which was not a classic success. Aunt Agatha captured East's queen with her king, cashed the ace of hearts, ruffed a heart and played three rounds of clubs on which she discarded the knave of diamonds and two hearts. Now a diamond was ruffed to leave the following position:

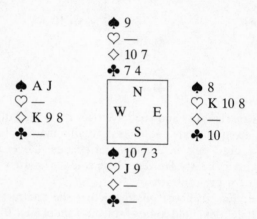

Aunt Agatha had won seven tricks and the defence one, so it only remained to play a heart from hand to ensure two more tricks. Aunt Agatha was cock-a-hoop after this hand. She had really enjoyed it, much to Issie's chagrin. 'She's so lucky,' he groaned, 'it's unbelievable. Still, I could have beaten it if only I'd cashed my two diamond winners and then played a third round for my partner to ruff high.'

'Could you really?' enquired Aunt Agatha, her eyebrows shooting up to the ceiling. 'Let's see how you do that. I overruff the queen of spades with my king, cash the ace of hearts, ruff a heart and play three rounds of clubs as before. This is the position:

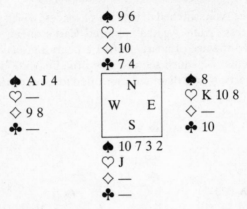

'I have won six tricks and you have two. I now lead the ten of diamonds from dummy. It doesn't really matter, but let's suppose Mildred puts in her eight of spades, I overruff and play the knave of hearts. However Issie defends I must make two more tricks for my contract.'

'Oh well, I'm glad we couldn't defeat the contract, then,' muttered Issie, delighted to be absolved from blame. But Aunt Agatha promptly turned and fixed him with her own inimitable stare.

'Who said you couldn't beat the contract?' she asked in quietly menacing tones.

'You did,' replied Issie foolishly.

'Nonsense, my dear Issie,' retorted Aunt Agatha. 'I said you couldn't beat the contract by cashing the ace and king of diamonds and then playing a third round. What you should have done was to play a low diamond at trick two.'

'But—' began Issie.

'But nothing,' interrupted Aunt Agatha. 'Just consider the diamonds that were missing—Q J 5 2. Surely Mildred's two on the first round was highly informative. Her holding had to be the singleton two, the queen and the two, or—improbably—the Q J 2. She would peter with J 2 or 5 2 but not with the Q 2. If you think about it, there was no way you could lose had you continued with a low diamond after the ace. Mildred would win and switch to a spade—now I must go down. Never mind, Issie, how could you expect to find the right answer when you failed to do so at the General Election?' said Aunt Agatha incongruously, giving Sally a broad wink. Issie, a staunch Labour supporter, was quite certain that Margaret Thatcher would not win the 1979 General Election, while Aunt Agatha, a vociferous and active Tory, had always maintained that Maggie would storm home. Having been proved right, Aunt Agatha never missed an opportunity to taunt Issie about his forecasting—if not actually his politics.

THE LAST SAY

If nothing else, this hand illustrates two important points: (1) You can have too many trumps in defence, when the only effect of the extra length is a restriction of choice; and (2) many players fail to consider the significance of small cards, but providing partner is a competent defender they can contribute a vital share to the whole defensive strategy.

5. Partnership with Aunt Agatha

We all have our crosses to bear. The fact that Aunt Agatha is a blood relation certainly doesn't make my life any easier. Logically there may be little reason for me to play bridge with my aunt, but that is not quite how she sees it. If you have ever had occasion to try to decipher the curious intricacies of female logic then you may have some sympathy for me.

I have always maintained that Alexander Graham Bell has much to answer for, and this thought flashed through my mind yet again when I picked up the telephone and heard the unmistakable voice of my aunt.

'Freddie, you are due to play a partnership with me.' The statement was unequivocal, and not even remotely interrogative. Indeed, it sounded more like a Royal Command. I was due to play a partnership with her. Now how had she worked that out?

Frantically I conjured up visions of having to dash off to Patagonia, or somewhere equally compelling, as I listened to Aunt Agatha in full cry. It was all perfectly logical to her. She wanted to play partnership. She was available. I am her nephew—sometimes called her favourite nephew—and because I hadn't played with her recently I was due to perform again. What could be simpler than that? Completely and utterly logical—to Aunt Agatha. Fool that I am, before you could say 'prior engagement' the date had somehow been agreed.

Once we had got to the starting-gate, as it were, it only remained for the fireworks to begin. After a few hands this deal turned up, and sure enough it was no ordinary squib.

Love all
Dealer North

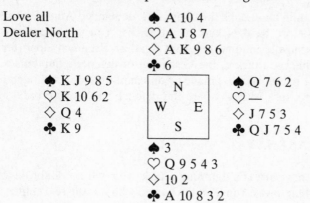

♠ A 10 4
♡ A J 8 7
◇ A K 9 8 6
♣ 6

♠ K J 9 8 5
♡ K 10 6 2
◇ Q 4
♣ K 9

♠ Q 7 6 2
♡ —
◇ J 7 5 3
♣ Q J 7 5 4

♠ 3
♡ Q 9 5 4 3
◇ 10 2
♣ A 10 8 3 2

The bidding:

S	W (A. A.)	N	E (F. N.)
—	—	1 ◇	No
1 ♡	1 ♠	2 ♠	3 ♠
4 ♣	4 ♠	6 ♡	No
No	No		

Perhaps our bidding helped them on their way, but the battle was by no means over yet. Aunt Agatha is too old a hand at the game to double, but I could sense the flames of aggression kindling in her nostrils.

The eight of spades was led, and declarer got off to a good start when he played the ace, ruffed a spade at trick two and then led the queen of hearts. Aunt Agatha and dummy played low, and I discarded a spade. South now realized that he needed four tricks from the diamond suit and duly led the two of diamonds. Aunt Agatha played the four, dummy the eight and, after a moment's thought, I won with the knave and switched to a club. But declarer was now home. He won the ace of clubs, played a heart to the eight, cashed the ace of diamonds, ruffed a spade and picked up Aunt Agatha's remaining trumps. Dummy was high.

'Why didn't you duck the diamond?' demanded Aunt Agatha almost before we'd picked up the tricks. You will appreciate from this hostile enquiry that Aunt Agatha is a staunch supporter of the theory 'attack is the best form of defence'. Diplomacy being my middle name, I made a non-committal reply although I was pretty sure I knew where the defence had really erred.

THE LAST SAY

Despite my partner's lightning attack, you will no doubt have noticed that it was Aunt Agatha herself who was the real culprit. Had she played the queen of diamonds on the first round, declarer would have been unable to extricate himself from the web. Come to think of it, South played well when leading the two of diamonds and not the ten.

As the rubbers progressed it was clear that the gods were looking on us with some disfavour. Things had been going poorly, and Aunt Agatha was beginning to get quite irritable. Well, more irritable than usual. It was something of a relief, therefore, to pick up the following hand:

♠ A K Q
♡ 6 4
◇ A K J 6
♣ A K J 8

At least this little collection should please her, I thought, as I recounted the points once more. Yes, they really did total 25. Enough to wipe the smile off the faces of the opponents when I opened 2 ♣. But wait. Aunt Agatha was the dealer at game all, and she opened 3 ♡. 'How annoying!' I mused. 'That means the grand slam will be too big a gamble. I'll have to settle for a comfortable six and prepare myself for Aunt Agatha's onslaught should it transpire that thirteen tricks are lay-down. At least that will be better than getting involved in a whole series of cue bids (any new suit from me now will be forcing), which will leave me little wiser in the end. Besides, Aunt Agatha likes straightforward methods.' So I bid 6 ♡. These were the two hands.

Game all
Dealer South

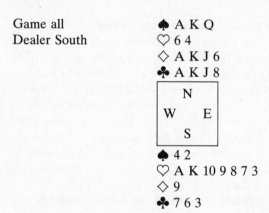

♠ A K Q
♡ 6 4
◇ A K J 6
♣ A K J 8

```
      N
  W       E
      S
```

♠ 4 2
♡ A K 10 9 8 7 3
◇ 9
♣ 7 6 3

This had been our simple bidding sequence:

S	N
3 ♡	6 ♡

Our opponents were a couple of tough campaigners—old pros, if you like—who knew their way around. Without much thought West led the ten of spades, and as dummy went down it was clear that Aunt Agatha liked what she saw. Indeed, the look she gave me seemed to echo the very fears I had had during the bidding. Without uttering a word she seemed to be saying, 'Why didn't you bid seven? Getting chicken in your old age?' Anyway, at trick two the whole scene changed dramatically. Aunt Agatha led a heart to her ace and East discarded a spade. My aunt now shot me a look which seemed to say, 'That's what comes of gambling on slams without proper trump support.' Or was I imagining it? Well, can Aunt Agatha still make her contract?

Being no mean performer at moments of crisis, she soon embarked on a plan to counter the vicious break. The idea was to reduce her trumps to the same number as West's, so that her last three cards would be ♡ K 10 9 while West would have ♡ Q J 5. In this event she would exit with the ten and claim the last two tricks.

The ace and king of diamonds were cashed, Aunt Agatha discarding a club, and the six of diamonds ruffed in hand, West following with the queen. On the ace and king of clubs East followed with the two and queen and West with the four and five. What now? Aunt Agatha, usually a quick player, paused for a long time before making her next move. If all the available evidence were to be taken at face value, then West had started life with a 2–4–3–4 shape. Thus it only remained to ruff a club, enter dummy with a spade and ruff a second club in order to achieve the desired ending. Having given each of her opponents a suspicious look in turn, Aunt Agatha played a club. But East followed suit, and West overruffed. A second trump trick had to be lost, so Aunt Agatha was one down.

This was the full hand:

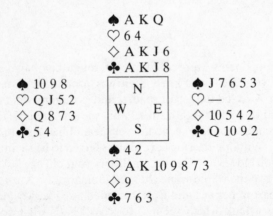

♠ A K Q
♡ 6 4
♢ A K J 6
♣ A K J 8

♠ 10 9 8   ♠ J 7 6 5 3
♡ Q J 5 2   ♡ —
♢ Q 8 7 3   ♢ 10 5 4 2
♣ 5 4   ♣ Q 10 9 2

♠ 4 2
♡ A K 10 9 8 7 3
♢ 9
♣ 7 6 3

It was easy for West to see that only the trump suit mattered, and East was not slow in picking up his cue when he saw his partner's false-card in diamonds. The queen of clubs was a nicely timed nail in the coffin and it only remained for Aunt Agatha to jump in. Although her suspicions were fully aroused, she can hardly be blamed for failing to find the successful line of play.

THE LAST SAY

The defence required in this case is analogous to the situation where you are prepared to give a series of ruff and discards because you know there are no tricks coming your way from the side suits. Naturally, you hope an extra trump trick, or tricks, will develop from the weakening process. Here the defence combined well when they quickly realized there was nothing for them on the side, but the day might still be saved if they laid one or two false trails. Had they followed suit Momma-Poppa fashion, then Aunt Agatha might have decided to ruff two diamonds and one master spade to reach this position:

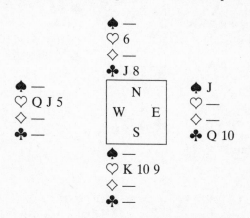

The lead of the ten of hearts restricts the defence to one trick.

After this hand there was an uncanny hush from Aunt Agatha's quarter of the table, a sign I knew well. Of course, Aunt Agatha was seething inwardly, furious that her opponents had outwitted her on a slam hand that she might well have made. This would not have been so bad had they made the slightest effort to mask their exuberance. But not a bit of it. They more than made up for our quietness. As Aunt Agatha said to me later: 'Their smugness was nauseating. The mutual admiration and self-congratulatory cross-talk, sitting there enveloped in their hallowed aura of superiority, made me want to throw up. No matter what happened I was determined to wipe that smugness off their faces and push it right down their oesophaguses.' Quite so! It's uncanny how Aunt Agatha always seems to get the right sort of hands when she is particularly anxious to teach her opponents a sharp lesson. This was the very next deal.

E–W game
Dealer West

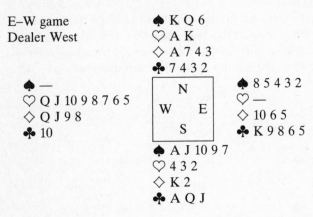

♠ K Q 6
♥ A K
♦ A 7 4 3
♣ 7 4 3 2

♠ —
♥ Q J 10 9 8 7 6 5
♦ Q J 9 8
♣ 10

♠ 8 5 4 3 2
♥ —
♦ 10 6 5
♣ K 9 8 6 5

♠ A J 10 9 7
♥ 4 3 2
♦ K 2
♣ A Q J

The bidding:

S (A. A.)	W	N (F. N.)	E
—	3 ♥	Dble	No
4 NT	No	5 ♥	No
5 NT	No	6 ♥	Dble
6 ♠	No	No	Dble
Rdble	No	No	No

I suppose East thought that if he doubled 6 ♡ and then 6 ♠
West would lead a heart, rather than regarding it as a Lightner
double which calls for an unusual lead, precluding a trump and
partner's suit. Even so, it's not quite clear from where the other
trick is supposed to emerge. Needless to say, Aunt Agatha had
redoubled almost before the double was out of East's mouth.

After a pregnant pause and a certain amount of fumbling,
West led the queen of hearts, which, if nothing else, proved that
the partnership was on the same wavelength. East ruffed the first
trick and returned the six of clubs. Can Aunt Agatha recover
from this body blow?

Having negotiated the club finesse successfully, declarer
played a spade to the king. When West showed out it seemed that
there was no longer a parking place for her third heart. Of
course, the clubs might divide 3–3 but this possibility was soon
ruled out when Aunt Agatha played a second club to her knave
and West discarded a heart. Trumps were drawn to arrive at the
following position:

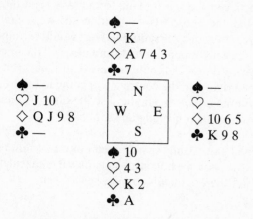

Aunt Agatha now played the ace of clubs, and, if I'm not very
much mistaken, she positively leered at West. Poor man, he was
such an unhappy defender. He had to play a card yet there was
nothing he could afford. If he threw a heart, Aunt Agatha would

play a heart to her king and then her four of hearts would be good. If he threw a diamond, then three rounds of diamonds would establish the suit and the king of hearts would provide the entry to cash the diamond winner.

'Let's see now, it was doubled and redoubled, wasn't it?' enquired Aunt Agatha innocently, turning her attention to East. East glared at her and muttered something under his breath. He was having a rough time from his partner because of the double, and was clearly in no mood for Aunt Agatha's barbs. However, Aunt Agatha seemed quite oblivious of the fires she had kindled so adroitly as she started to count out in a loud voice: '180, 360, $720 + 50 = 770 + 500 = 1270$. Not bad, considering everything. Not bad at all!'

THE LAST SAY

East's final double was quite asinine. If Aunt Agatha's bidding was to be believed she was looking for a grand slam, not just a small one, so the prospects of beating six were not great. Furthermore, after East's first double West would certainly have led a heart, since his opponents had announced all the first-round controls and any other lead could be very dangerous. But even if East had been right and the contract was going to fail by a trick, the gain from the double would be just 50 points. A bad return for the possibility of conceding an extra 590.

The next hand gave Aunt Agatha even more pleasure than the last. On this occasion she not only had to play it immaculately but she had to get the opponents to help her as well.

Game all   (F. N.)
Dealer North   ♠ K 6
                            ♡ K 4 3
                            ◇ A 4
                            ♣ A K J 10 9 6

(A. A.)
♠ A Q 5 4 3 2
♡ A Q 6
◇ K Q 7
♣ 8

It didn't take us long to arrive in 7 NT, played of course by Aunt Agatha. West led the knave of diamonds. What plans should declarer make?

If the spades break there is no problem, for all the tricks are on top. But if they don't break declarer will have to turn her attention to the club suit. And how should she play the clubs?

This was the full deal:

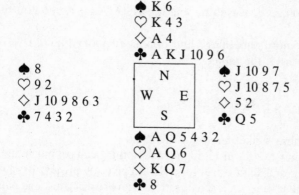

Aunt Agatha won the diamond lead in dummy and tested the spades, discovering that East held four of them. She now cashed her red-suit winners in an effort to find out as much about the hand as possible. This little exercise told her that East had started life with four spades, two diamonds and five hearts—and therefore two clubs. West, who knew all about the diamond suit early on, threw diamonds each time he had to make a discard. Thus at the critical moment when Aunt Agatha had to tackle the clubs she knew that West held four and East two. Furthermore, she realized that if West held the queen of clubs she could not make the required four tricks from the suit. Therefore she had to play East for Q x. Without further ado Aunt Agatha cashed the ace and king of clubs—and claimed all the tricks.

'That was an extraordinary play,' muttered East. 'Not finessing the club, I mean.'

'I know,' replied Aunt Agatha wickedly. 'You want to talk to your partner about it.'

'What has it got to do with me?' demanded West belligerently.

'Only that you forced me to take the winning line,' retorted Aunt Agatha, thoroughly enjoying herself. 'Had you thrown one little club you would have presented me with an option. As it was, you played the suit for me. Thank you very much. Now let's see, 1500 . . . It wasn't doubled, was it?' Aunt Agatha burbled on.

You know something? Our opponents looked quite relieved when we left the table.

THE LAST SAY

Two points strike me about this hand.

1. When the reward is high—and nothing can get much higher than a grand slam—everyone should give the project Big Deal Treatment. It is not just a question of an overtrick in some paltry part-score contract. It is the real business. The equivalent of a

meeting of heads of state, if you like. So if West really gets his thinking cap on he may well decide to let one club go before the critical point in the play is reached.

2. Although Aunt Agatha's reasoning cannot be faulted, the other side of the coin is not without interest. Suppose West had started life with ♣ Q x x x, then of course it might be fatal to part with one of them. So any West throwing a club and retaining a worthless diamond would surely be marked down as a player who had either taken leave of his senses or could not possibly hold that vital queen. Thus the play of the ace and king of clubs would still be marked. That said, West can only play as well as the circumstances permit and hope that declarer's thought processes are of an inferior nature.

Maybe you are wondering why it is that I never seem to play any hands of interest. It is nothing to do with the Sex Discrimination Act. Nothing at all. In fact it is nothing to do with sex. It's just that Aunt Agatha likes playing the hands and years of keeping dubious company have taught me that it's often better to allow a pulling horse a little rein. Fight the beast and he'll pull harder, work himself into a lather and God knows where you'll finish up. Kid him that you are giving him his head and you'll exercise a tolerable measure of control. Roughly speaking that describes the circumstances applicable to my aunt. Do you wonder then that I actually try to steer contracts her way?

My halo shone extra brightly on the following hand when I made no effort to play the final contract:

Love all
Dealer North

> ♠ A 9 8 7
> ♡ Q J 5
> ◇ A K Q
> ♣ A Q 10

```
        N
    W       E
        S
```

> ♠ 4
> ♡ K 9 6 4 3 2
> ◇ 7 5 4
> ♣ K J 8

The bidding:

S	W	N	E
(A. A.)		(F. N.)	
—	—	2 ♣	No
2 ◇	No	2 NT	No
3 ♡	No	4 ♡	No
4 NT	No	5 ♠	No
6 ♡	Dble	No	No
No			

The queen of spades was led. How should Aunt Agatha plan the play?

This was the complete deal:

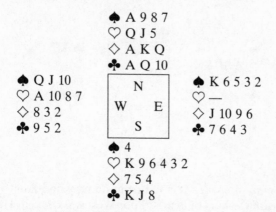

♠ A 9 8 7
♡ Q J 5
◇ A K Q
♣ A Q 10

♠ Q J 10
♡ A 10 8 7
◇ 8 3 2
♣ 9 5 2

♠ K 6 5 3 2
♡ —
◇ J 10 9 6
♣ 7 6 4 3

♠ 4
♡ K 9 6 4 3 2
◇ 7 5 4
♣ K J 8

'Where are your twenty-three points?' demanded Aunt Agatha, as the dummy went down.

'I allowed half a point for the ten of clubs and another half-point in case you played the hand,' I lied with a straight face. And then, as Aunt Agatha gave me a withering look: 'I know your play is worth more than half a point but you usually adjust your own bidding to accommodate that factor.'

Aunt Agatha didn't seem to hear. She was concentrating on the two hands.

She won the spade lead in dummy, ruffed a spade and led a low heart. The queen of hearts won, and when East threw a spade Aunt Agatha was visibly shaken. A minute or two later, however, she had found a viable plan—Lady Luck willing. Aunt Agatha ruffed a second spade, then cashed three clubs and three diamonds to arrive at the following position, North to play:

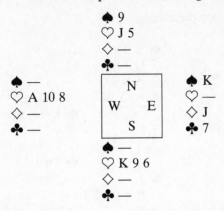

The nine of spades was led from dummy and Aunt Agatha ruffed with the king of hearts. Poor West was cooked. He could make the ace of hearts, but that was the only trick the defence could muster.

'Only half a point for my play, indeed! Damned impertinence, I call it,' admonished Aunt Agatha.

THE LAST SAY

In practice Aunt Agatha's play was worth much more than half a point, and West's double even more again! Without the alarm bells ringing, declarer would probably have played the queen of hearts from dummy at trick two rather than opening up the possibilities of a ruff or trump promotion by trying to get to hand with a club or a spade ruff. Alerted by the double, however, the 5 per cent chance of West holding all the outstanding trumps suddenly became a warm favourite. That the remaining suits were distributed kindly was perhaps no more than both sides deserved.

If nothing else, partnership with Aunt Agatha keeps one on one's toes. Not so much because of the bridge—that more or less

falls into shape—but because Aunt Agatha is a person of moods
and has a very acid tongue. If you want a peaceful life it's
advisable to humour her as much as possible, and watch that
tongue! Me, I go for the peaceful life. Luckily one can choose
one's friends but, sadly, one cannot choose one's relatives.
Having a relative who is dotty about bridge, like Aunt Agatha,
gets you over a barrel. It is certainly a strange feeling playing with
her. Euphemistically speaking, we were still in partnership
though we had suffered a few set-backs since Aunt Agatha's
success in 6 ♡. Without putting too fine a point on it, Aunt
Agatha was steadily getting into another foul mood. Then, up
cropped this hand.

Love all   ♠ A K J 8 5
Dealer West   ♡ A Q 7 4
                            ◇ Q 4
                            ♣ 10 6

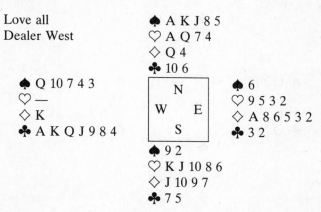

♠ Q 10 7 4 3   ♠ 6
♡ —   ♡ 9 5 3 2
◇ K   ◇ A 8 6 5 3 2
♣ A K Q J 9 8 4   ♣ 3 2

                            ♠ 9 2
                            ♡ K J 10 8 6
                            ◇ J 10 9 7
                            ♣ 7 5

The bidding:

S	W	N	E
(A. A.)		(F. N.)	
—	1 ♣	Dble	No
1 ♡	1 ♠	2 ♡	No
3 ♡	4 ♣	4 ♡	No
No	No		

Aunt Agatha's bid of 3 ♡ is one of her specials, known as the
Aunt Agatha two-way trial bid. If ten tricks are there, it will be

my fault if I don't give her game. If nine tricks are the limit, it is my fault if I go on. Quite a simple convention really. Fortunately West came to my rescue and I would be able to claim that my 4 ♡ bid was competitive.

West cashed two top clubs and switched to the four of spades. After some thought Aunt Agatha successfully ran the spade round to her nine. However, she was not out of the wood yet. After all, there were four top losers, and when the trumps broke badly the outlook seemed bleak.

Anyway, the trumps were drawn, giving Aunt Agatha five tricks and the defence two. This was the position with South to lead:

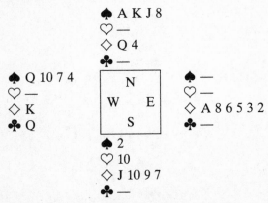

Was it my imagination or did I detect a gleam in Aunt Agatha's eye as she took stock? Yes, there was no doubt about it. Even the beginnings of a smile touched her lips. The mood hadn't changed for nothing. Something was up. Something important. Suddenly the ten of hearts hit the table and the world seemed to stand still as West considered this unpalatable development. Unable to part with a spade, or a diamond, he reluctantly threw the queen of clubs. Dummy and East discarded diamonds. But now a spade to the eight followed by the queen of diamonds left the defence powerless. East could win and concede the rest of the tricks to Aunt Agatha, or West could win and concede the rest to dummy.

'You're a racing man, Freddie—is that what you call an each-way chance?' enquired Aunt Agatha.

THE LAST SAY

You couldn't really call West's defence inspired, since South was unlikely to have both a heart suit and the ace of diamonds. Indeed, the ace of diamonds with East must figure at short odds. Had West persevered with this line of thought and attempted to cash his king of diamonds before playing a spade, all his problems would have been over. But then Aunt Agatha would never have enjoyed her exciting end-play.

On the next exhibit there was a strange bidding sequence.

Game all
Dealer South

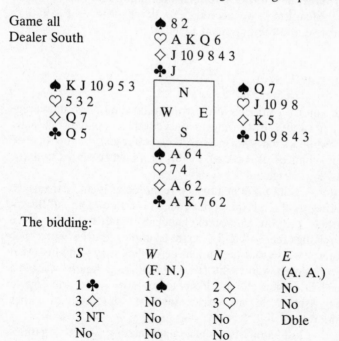

♠ 8 2
♡ A K Q 6
♢ J 10 9 8 4 3
♣ J

♠ K J 10 9 5 3
♡ 5 3 2
♢ Q 7
♣ Q 5

♠ Q 7
♡ J 10 9 8
♢ K 5
♣ 10 9 8 4 3

♠ A 6 4
♡ 7 4
♢ A 6 2
♣ A K 7 6 2

The bidding:

S	W	N	E
	(F. N.)		(A. A.)
1 ♣	1 ♠	2 ♢	No
3 ♢	No	3 ♡	No
3 NT	No	No	Dble
No	No	No	

Aunt Agatha loves to direct operations so her double and somewhat ungracious remarks to me later on came as no surprise.

'I thought I had better double to stop you making some daft lead,' she explained in her forthright way. Well, she got the spade lead all right, as requested by the double, but what do you think about the contract? Will declarer succeed or will he fail?

I led the knave of spades which Aunt Agatha covered with the queen. Declarer ducked the first two rounds of spades and won the third, on which dummy discarded the six of hearts. But what should Aunt Agatha discard? A heart looks safe and a club by no means fatal. However, Aunt Agatha had other ideas. She discarded a diamond—not the five but the king!

Poor South, there was no way he could recover from this body-blow. Seven tricks were his maximum, and that's what he took. Meantime, we scored 500, thanks to Aunt Agatha's enterprise and the opponent's lack of it.

THE LAST SAY

Have you ever noticed in the rough-and-tumble of an average game of rubber bridge how many a contract is played in a hairy 3 NT while a small slam in a suit would offer just as good, or even better, chances of success? In this particular case 6 ♢, as the cards lie, is frigid.

Aunt Agatha's double must be regarded as highly dangerous. It looked as though the opponents had settled in an indifferent contract, but on the other hand it might be a lay-down (interchange the ♡ K and ♢ Q for example). Furthermore, there was a grave risk that they might be pushed into something that was completely watertight. It's true that Aunt Agatha wanted a spade lead, which she was likely to get anyway, but the urge to direct partner at all costs must be tempered by other considerations.

Eagle-eyed analysts, while appreciating Aunt Agatha's

thoughtful discard of the king of diamonds, will have noticed that declarer can always make his contract. Suppose he reads West for a six-card spade suit, which seems quite probable on the bidding. Now all he has to do is to win the second spade and then play the diamond suit so as to prevent West from obtaining the lead. He must cross to dummy with a heart at trick three and lead a diamond towards his own hand. If East plays low, then the ace and another diamond is the winning play. If East contributes the king, then she must be allowed to hold this trick, and the ace must be played when the declarer regains the lead.

If you are one of those people who feel slightly uncomfortable when doubling little old ladies who overbid, you may dismiss all such thoughts from your mind when you meet my Aunt Agatha. She may look demure and kindly, providing nothing has upset her, but underneath that outward disguise is a pretty tough and resourceful operator. On the following hand East doubled in the voice of a man who thought the final contract had about as much chance of success as that curiously conceived piece of Alice in Wonderland legislation decreeing that picketing must be carried out in a peaceful manner.

Game all
Dealer West

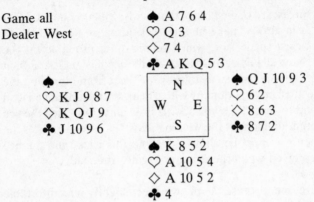

```
                      ♠ A 7 6 4
                      ♡ Q 3
                      ◇ 7 4
                      ♣ A K Q 5 3
    ♠ —                             ♠ Q J 10 9 3
    ♡ K J 9 8 7           N         ♡ 6 2
    ◇ K Q J 9         W       E     ◇ 8 6 3
    ♣ J 10 9 6            S         ♣ 8 7 2
                      ♠ K 8 5 2
                      ♡ A 10 5 4
                      ◇ A 10 5 2
                      ♣ 4
```

The bidding:

S	W	N	E
(A. A.)		(F. N.)	
—	1 ♡	Dble	No
2 ♡	No	3 ♣	No
3 ♠	No	4 ♠	Dble
No	No	No	

West led the king of diamonds and when this card was allowed to win the trick East must have viewed his prospects with some enthusiasm. However, Aunt Agatha won the diamond continuation, ruffed a diamond, and cashed the ace of hearts and three top clubs, throwing two hearts from her hand. This was the position after the first seven tricks. It is dummy to lead; the defence have one trick and Aunt Agatha six.

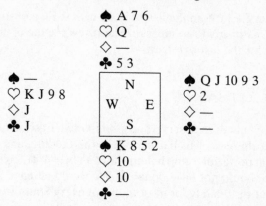

When dummy played the three of clubs East looked a little
uneasy for the first time. If he ruffs high, South ditches her losing
heart and subsequently loses just one trump trick. If he ruffs low,
South overruffs, leads a spade to dummy's ace and plays the five
of clubs which East must ruff. But now South throws her losing
heart and has only one more trick to lose. So East threw a heart
on the three of clubs and Aunt Agatha ruffed. A diamond was
ruffed in dummy and overruffed by East, who played the queen
of spades, won by dummy's ace. Now the five of clubs put the
final skids under East in the following end-game. This time the
defence have two tricks and declarer eight:

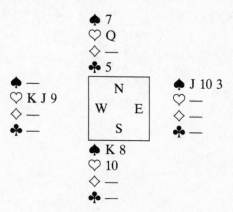

In fact East ruffed the five of clubs with the ten of spades, but Aunt Agatha made no mistake. She threw the ten of hearts and waited for the last two tricks.

THE LAST SAY

If opponents ever deserve one's sympathy, East certainly gets mine in this case. His partner opens the bidding, and yet even with that powerful trump holding he can't beat 4 ♠. I refuse to say that he should not have doubled. We would all have done just that, but fortunately for most of us not every South would have been an Aunt Agatha.

On the next offering Aunt Agatha showed shrewd judgement to land her contract.

N–S game
Dealer East

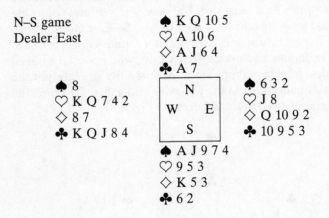

```
                    ♠ K Q 10 5
                    ♡ A 10 6
                    ◇ A J 6 4
                    ♣ A 7
    ♠ 8                           ♠ 6 3 2
    ♡ K Q 7 4 2      N            ♡ J 8
    ◇ 8 7         W     E         ◇ Q 10 9 2
    ♣ K Q J 8 4      S            ♣ 10 9 5 3
                    ♠ A J 9 7 4
                    ♡ 9 5 3
                    ◇ K 5 3
                    ♣ 6 2
```

The bidding:

S (A. A.)	W	N (F. N.)	E
—	—	—	No
No	1 ♡	Dble	No
2 ♠	3 ♣	4 ♠	No
No	No		

West, in love with his shape, left nothing unbid, although as is so often the case this may well have been his undoing. At first glance it appears that there are four inescapable losers—two hearts, one diamond and one club—but Aunt Agatha soon found a way of losing a loser, or, if you prefer, gaining a winner.

The king of clubs was led and won in dummy. Three rounds of spades followed, West discarding a heart and a club. Next came the ace and then the king of diamonds to arrive at the critical point of the play. Aunt Agatha had to decide whether to lead a third diamond towards the knave, hoping that West was 1-5-3-4, or set about eliminating the hand on the basis that West was 1-5-2-5. When diamonds were played neither opponent had petered, which was not particularly significant. However, Aunt Agatha had not overlooked the fact that West had been very chatty during the auction, which suggested a shapely hand, especially as there were only fourteen points at large. There was one further clue to the distribution—East might have bid on in clubs had he held five of them. So, having failed to bring down the doubleton queen of diamonds, Aunt Agatha now exited with a club. East won this trick, switched to the knave of hearts, which was allowed to hold, and continued with the eight of hearts, dummy's ace taking West's queen.

These were the last four cards. It is North to play and the defence have two tricks:

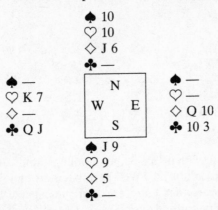

Dummy's last heart was played, and West had to concede a ruff and discard which provided a parking place for Aunt Agatha's losing diamond.

THE LAST SAY

At duplicate bridge East–West might have saved in 5 ♣ which would have cost 500. At rubber bridge, when a game down, such tactics are seldom worth while. It is better to lose gracefully, pay up and start a new rubber. There is also the other side of the coin. Too much exuberance during the bidding can so easily pin-point the winning line in play. That is what happened here, and although it is not a hard hand the successful conclusion gave Aunt Agatha much pleasure. It also put her in great shape for the next test.

Our bidding may not have been entirely without blemish on the following deal, but Aunt Agatha soon made up for any shortcomings with a sparkling piece of dummy play.

Game all   ♠ A J 3
Dealer West   ♡ Q J 7 2
                ◇ Q 5 4 3
                ♣ 8 2

                ♠ K 10 8 2
                ♡ A 10 8 6
                ◇ K 10 7 6
                ♣ J

The bidding:

S	W	N	E
(A. A.)		(F. N.)	
—	1 ♣	No	2 ♣
Dble	3 ♣	4 ♣	No
4 ♡	No	No	No

West started with the ace and king of clubs. East played the three and four and Aunt Agatha ruffed the second round. A small diamond to the queen, which held, was followed by three rounds of hearts, East's doubleton king being successfully finessed. The third trump was won in dummy, East throwing the seven of clubs, and a diamond was led to South's ten and West's knave. West now played the queen of clubs. How should declarer continue?

Aunt Agatha had given the matter a lot of thought and, as she told me later: 'I really knew the location of every vital card.' West was marked with three hearts and three diamonds, and since East had not responded one spade it seemed likely that he held no more than four. This left West with a doubleton spade and five clubs headed by the three top honours. Moving to East, who could be placed with a 4–2–2–5 shape, he had shown up with just the king of hearts so it seemed probable that he held the queen of spades as well. On the basis of this analysis Aunt Agatha was ready to proceed. Are you? This was the full deal:

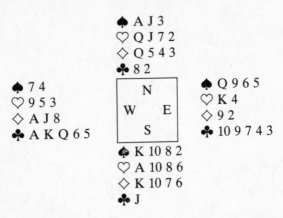

♠ A J 3
♥ Q J 7 2
♦ Q 5 4 3
♣ 8 2

♠ 7 4
♥ 9 5 3
♦ A J 8
♣ A K Q 6 5

♠ Q 9 6 5
♥ K 4
♦ 9 2
♣ 10 9 7 4 3

♠ K 10 8 2
♥ A 10 8 6
♦ K 10 7 6
♣ J

Aunt Agatha ruffed the queen of clubs (West would have done better to underlead this card, leaving the declarer in some doubt as to its location) with dummy's last trump and discarded a diamond from her own hand. She now made the key play—the knave of spades from dummy, no other card will do. East covered with the queen and South the king. Finally the two of spades was led to dummy's ace and the three led back towards her hand. When East followed with the six of spades Aunt Agatha played the eight and started to collect the trick before West had even played a card. It only remained to cash the ten of spades and concede the last diamond before adding up the rubber.

THE LAST SAY

I concede that we left absolutely nothing unbid and have now probably offended a few purists as well, but I am unrepentant because it brought out the very best in Aunt Agatha. Seldom are declarers so sure-footed, or the cards read with such astuteness. If bridge with my aunt always went so smoothly it would be a pleasure to play with her . . . sometimes. As a matter of fact my luck held out for one more hand—the last of the evening.

Although the final deal was bid and defended in a slightly euphoric haze—it had been a hot day and the drinks had been flying around—Aunt Agatha once again handled the dummy brilliantly.

N–S game
Dealer South

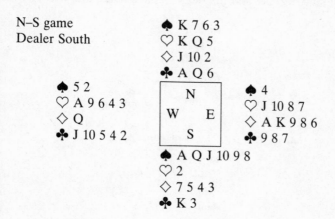

```
                    ♠ K 7 6 3
                    ♡ K Q 5
                    ◇ J 10 2
                    ♣ A Q 6
  ♠ 5 2                              ♠ 4
  ♡ A 9 6 4 3          N             ♡ J 10 8 7
  ◇ Q            W          E        ◇ A K 9 8 6
  ♣ J 10 5 4 2         S            ♣ 9 8 7
                    ♠ A Q J 10 9 8
                    ♡ 2
                    ◇ 7 5 4 3
                    ♣ K 3
```

The bidding:

S	W	N	E
(A. A.)		(F. N.)	
3 ♠	No	4 ♠	Dble!
No	5 ♣	Dble	No
5 ♠!	No	No	No

Of course, Aunt Agatha's final bid beggars description, as does her excuse for making it. 'I knew we would defeat them, Freddie, but I was tired, had won enough, and wanted to go home.' To Aunt Agatha that was a perfectly logical reason for playing in 5 ♠, and with East's defence little better than his bidding she still claims complete justification.

West led the queen of diamonds and, inexplicably, East failed to overtake, which was to prove a very costly error. The club switch was won by South and trumps drawn in two rounds. Now Aunt Agatha played her singleton heart towards dummy. If West played his ace, then dummy would provide three discards for the losing diamonds—so he ducked. The small heart was now ruffed and dummy's two clubs cashed to arrive at the following position. It is dummy to play and the defence have taken one trick:

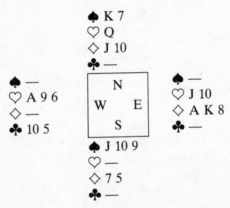

♠ K 7
♡ Q
◇ J 10
♣ —

♠ —   ♠ —
♡ A 9 6   ♡ J 10
◇ —   W E   ◇ A K 8
♣ 10 5   ♣ —

♠ J 10 9
♡ —
◇ 7 5
♣ —

With the look of a player who knows exactly what she is doing, Aunt Agatha played the queen of hearts and discarded a diamond from her hand. West won this trick, but then had to concede a ruff and discard to give declarer her contract.

'Don't forget the hundred honours, Freddie,' chortled Aunt Agatha, thoroughly pleased with herself.

THE LAST SAY

It is bids like Aunt Agatha's five spades that make my hair go greyer faster than nature intended. True she opened a slightly off-beat 3 ♠ but that doesn't alter the fact that her partner was in charge and his decision—to double—must be final. That is only logical. There are no ifs and no buts. Just one thing however— no one ever takes charge of Aunt Agatha. She makes her own rules, designed to control others, not impede her. And they are strictly unilateral.

6. A 'Friendly' Rubber at the Club

Dropping in at the club for a friendly rubber is a pursuit enjoyed by many thousands of people all over the world. Most of the time most of the people complete the exercise without much more than the occasional ripple. In Aunt Agatha's case, however, a ripple is more or less inevitable, while a tidal wave is no forlorn outsider. Of course, the cards can be perverse, the luck excruciating and partner positively moronic—these things happen, and Aunt Agatha is not slow to react adversely to any one of them. But it is certain personalities, especially when they are playing against her, that bug Aunt Agatha most.

One day, towards the end of the afternoon session, I called in at the club to see my aunt and found her sitting in a corner, glaring into space. Something had upset her, that was sure.

'Oh dear, oh dear, you look as though you've had a disastrous game and lost at least thirty or forty pence. I could arrange a loan,' I offered flippantly.

Aunt Agatha barely acknowledged my greeting. Instead she fixed me with a steely gaze. It was clear that I had earned no marks for tact or psychology. However, *I* was not really the source of Aunt Agatha's annoyance, and as she is seldom diverted from her main target for long her glare quickly left my face and focused on some object across the room.

'Come on,' I said soothingly, 'tell Freddie all about it.'

Following my aunt's gaze I noticed a table in play, where Mildred was partnering some unknown guy against a couple of formidable-looking females.

'Who are the birds?' I enquired, sensing that somehow they had been the major source of irritation.

'Those harridans,' proclaimed Aunt Agatha, obviously needing no further identification, 'are visitors, and the sooner they crawl back under their favourite stone the better I shall like it. The KGB in drag, I call them.'

Soon the grisly details were pouring forth.* This was the first hand that Aunt Agatha had found hard to stomach. She had cut Mildred against the KGB, whom we'll code-name Gert and Daisy.

Love all
Dealer South

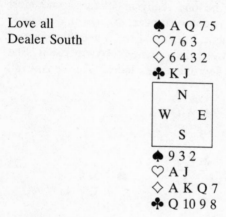

♠ A Q 7 5
♥ 7 6 3
♦ 6 4 3 2
♣ K J

♠ 9 3 2
♥ A J
♦ A K Q 7
♣ Q 10 9 8

The bidding:

S	N
(Mildred)	(A. A.)
1 ♦	1 ♠
1 NT	3 NT

Daisy, West, led the two of hearts to Gert's queen. How should Mildred plan the play?

---

* In order to capture the atmosphere and give an approximate indication of the looks and verbal exchanges, I must admit to a degree of cheating. Later that evening, when Aunt Agatha had gone home, I went over the hands again with Mildred and the KGB. The latter, incidentally, were nothing like so fearsome away from the table as Aunt Agatha would have me believe.

Mildred did not see any great problem. If the two of hearts was a genuine card then the suit was divided 4–4. So at trick two she proceeded to knock out the ace of clubs. West won the second round and continued hearts, to East's king. East returned a heart, enabling the defence to take three hearts and the ace of clubs, Mildred discarding two spades. After studying the position for a few moments Daisy led the eight of spades, and it was now Mildred's turn to huddle. Her woman's instinct, that indefinable quality that no one really understands and most males dismiss with a contemptuous sneer, told her that the king of spades was probably right. But did she really need the finesse? After all, the diamonds were likely to break, so why risk it? She didn't—and her contract flew out of the window. This was the full deal:

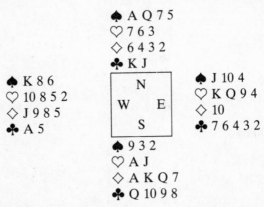

♠ A Q 7 5
♥ 7 6 3
♦ 6 4 3 2
♣ K J

♠ K 8 6
♥ 10 8 5 2
♦ J 9 8 5
♣ A 5

N
W   E
S

♠ J 10 4
♥ K Q 9 4
♦ 10
♣ 7 6 4 3 2

♠ 9 3 2
♥ A J
♦ A K Q 7
♣ Q 10 9 8

With the diamonds failing to break, Mildred was left without further resource, and that was +50 to Gert and Daisy.

'I played it with the odds, you know, partner,' blurted Mildred, conscious of Aunt Agatha's frowning disapproval. 'The spade finesse is only a 50 per cent chance and the diamond break is something much higher—nearly 70 per cent, I think.'

Gert and Daisy were highly delighted with their success, and Daisy in particular was not prepared to let the hand go by without blowing her own trumpet.

'I knew the diamonds weren't breaking so I thought I would put her under pressure in spades before she learnt the bad news,' explained Daisy, quite unnecessarily, as everyone had seen the position.

Gert beamed and, giving her partner an approving smile, seemed about to say something when Aunt Agatha chimed in with a cutting observation.

'Don't delude yourself that you played with the odds, Mildred. You didn't. What you did do was to provide the defence with a Momma-Poppa opportunity to restrict your options. Even two beginners would hardly have failed that test.'

Aunt Agatha's acid comments at least had the effect of silencing Gert and Daisy, but Mildred—although perhaps she should have known better—was not convinced and still harboured a sense of grievance.

'Are you saying that a 50 per cent chance is better than a—er—70 per cent chance?' stammered Mildred suspiciously.

'Of course not. I am saying that two chances are better than one. All you had to do was test the diamonds before you knocked out the ace of clubs, then you would have known whether or not you required the spade finesse. That way you would have combined your chances.'

THE LAST SAY

Aunt Agatha had certainly hit the nail on the head. While Mildred was right that the spade finesse (a 50 per cent chance) was inferior to the 3–2 break in diamonds (68 per cent), both lines, played individually, were inferior to the combination of the two (84 per cent). In order to enjoy this advantage Mildred should have played two rounds of diamonds before knocking out the ace of clubs.

An interesting situation would have arisen had there been one top diamond in dummy. Something like this:

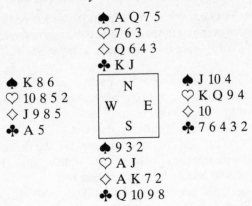

Suppose the play goes the same way to the first three tricks: ♡ A, ♣ K and ♣ J to West's ace. West must be careful not to rock the boat. Should she continue with a second heart declarer can prevail. Let's say that the heart tricks are cashed and declarer hops up with the ace of spades on West's eight. Now when the clubs are run West is squeezed in diamonds and spades. This will be the position before the last club is cashed:

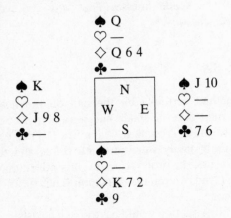

In order to avoid this ending, West must switch to a low spade at trick four.

The next hand did little to bring Aunt Agatha and Mildred together on a harmonious note. (The seating arrangements change from hand to hand so that the declarer, in traditional fashion, always occupies the South seat.)

Love all
Dealer East

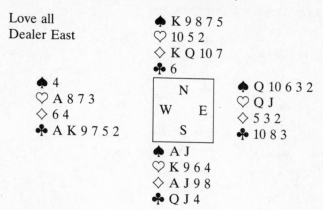

♠ K 9 8 7 5
♡ 10 5 2
◇ K Q 10 7
♣ 6

♠ 4
♡ A 8 7 3
◇ 6 4
♣ A K 9 7 5 2

♠ Q 10 6 3 2
♡ Q J
◇ 5 3 2
♣ 10 8 3

♠ A J
♡ K 9 6 4
◇ A J 9 8
♣ Q J 4

The bidding:

S (Gert)	W (Mildred)	N (Daisy)	E (A. A.)
1 ◇	2 ♣	2 ♠	No
2 NT	No	3 NT	No
No	No		

Mildred led the seven of clubs to Aunt Agatha's ten and declarer's queen. Gert must have thought her chances pretty slim as she counted the sure winners. Four diamonds, one club and two spades—three if the queen of spades was right. So at best that was only eight tricks—or was it? Anyway, she began well by playing a diamond to the king and then taking the spade finesse. The ace of spades and a diamond to the queen enabled Gert to shed a heart on the king of spades. Mildred completed a peter in diamonds and discarded the eight and three of hearts on the ♠ A K, while Aunt Agatha followed to everything in natural order.

Gert now cashed the ♦ A J, and Mildred had to find two more discards. The two of clubs came easily enough, but then she had to decide between the seven of hearts and a club. Fingering first the heart and then the small club, she eventually settled for the latter, to leave the following position:

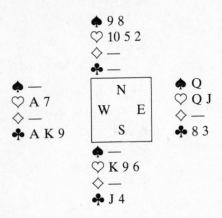

```
                    ♠ 9 8
                    ♡ 10 5 2
                    ♦ —
                    ♣ —
    ♠ —            ┌─────────┐        ♠ Q
    ♡ A 7          │    N    │        ♡ Q J
    ♦ —            │  W   E  │        ♦ —
    ♣ A K 9        │    S    │        ♣ 8 3
                   └─────────┘
                    ♠ —
                    ♡ K 9 6
                    ♦ —
                    ♣ J 4
```

When declarer exited with the knave of clubs the defence had to capitulate, as nothing could prevent Gert making the king of hearts for her ninth trick.

'Sorry,' muttered Mildred, noting Aunt Agatha's expression. 'I thought you had the king of hearts and I simply could not tell whether you had two clubs or three.'

'I don't know what gave you the idea that I had the king of hearts,' replied Aunt Agatha tersely, 'but one thing is certain: if declarer started with ♡ K x x and ♣ Q J x x there is no way you could beat the contract, so you might just as well play her for three clubs. Even if you throw away the nine of clubs and keep the five, that would be enough to ditch her.'

'But I had to make my discard on the fourth diamond before you,' retaliated Mildred, somewhat illogically.

'Exactly,' retorted Aunt Agatha, 'when I fail to discard a high heart you can be pretty sure that I have not got the king, so you must play me for the eight of clubs. You underlead, I win and cash my queen of spades, and that's that. I don't even need the knave of hearts.'

While Aunt Agatha and Mildred were having their say the opposition were indulging in some mutual admiration. Although ostensibly fully occupied with Mildred, Aunt Agatha was not unaware of her opponents' cockiness, or of their cross-chat, which she found distinctly nauseating. But they had just made three notrumps on a meagre 24 count, and Gert had had to play it well to get home. It was only natural therefore that they should express some measure of satisfaction.

'Sorry I was a bit thin for my raise,' apologized Daisy, 'but I knew if anyone could make it you would.'

'You bid it beautifully,' gushed Gert. 'Once the spade finesse was right I was pretty confident.' And then, catching sight of Aunt Agatha's withering look, she added: 'Of course, it was terribly difficult for them to get the defence right.' This patronizing comment did nothing to ease the tension, or lessen the ferocity of Aunt Agatha's expression.

THE LAST SAY

The critical point of the defence is whether or not East has the king of hearts. If East has this card, it really does not matter whether declarer has four clubs or three. This must be obvious to West and should not be altogether obscure to East. Maybe it is a somewhat esoteric point, but suppose for a moment that East does hold $\heartsuit$ K x x. Now, surely, on the king of spades she should drop the queen! That will make West sit up and take notice—and of course it is perfectly safe. It follows, therefore, in a keen partnership, that failure to be demonstrative in the only suit where it is possible to ring bells (spades) should suggest an unhelpful holding in hearts. Thus if West is on the same wavelength as East she will have to assume that her clubs will run. If they don't, and it turns out that East does hold the king of hearts after all, then at least West will be well placed in the post mortem. As things were, it was Aunt Agatha who was comfortably poised and Mildred who was wriggling.

Aunt Agatha played the next hand well to make it game all.

E–W game
Dealer South

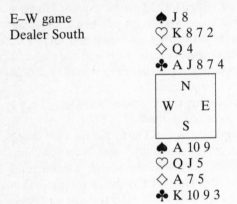

♠ J 8
♡ K 8 7 2
◇ Q 4
♣ A J 8 7 4

♠ A 10 9
♡ Q J 5
◇ A 7 5
♣ K 10 9 3

This was the bidding:

S	N
(A. A.)	(Mildred)
1 NT	2 ♣
2 ◇	2 NT
3 NT	

West, Gert, led the two of diamonds. Aunt Agatha tried the queen from dummy, but Daisy covered with the king and Aunt Agatha was forced to win with the ace (it would be dangerous to duck as that would give the defence the chance of winning three diamonds, one spade and one heart). The queen of hearts won the next trick, but when Aunt Agatha continued with the knave East won and played back the ten of hearts, West throwing a spade. How should declarer continue?

You'll observe that it is now essential for Aunt Agatha to guess the lie of the club suit, since she cannot afford to lose a trick to the queen. This was the full deal:

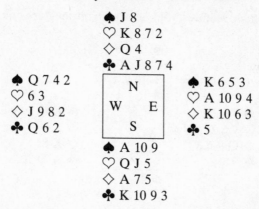

♠ J 8
♡ K 8 7 2
◇ Q 4
♣ A J 8 7 4

♠ Q 7 4 2
♡ 6 3
◇ J 9 8 2
♣ Q 6 2

♠ K 6 5 3
♡ A 10 9 4
◇ K 10 6 3
♣ 5

♠ A 10 9
♡ Q J 5
◇ A 7 5
♣ K 10 9 3

Aunt Agatha wasted little time in playing a club to her king and then, as though she could see through the backs of the cards, ran the ten of clubs when West played low. And that was nine tricks in the bag.

'What a lucky guess!' exclaimed Gert unwisely. 'I thought the odds favoured playing for the drop with nine cards.'

'Oh, they do,' retorted Aunt Agatha, 'they certainly do—except when one opponent has the queen to three!'

Well, did you make an inspired guess?

THE LAST SAY

Of course, it was hardly an inspired guess. Aunt Agatha knew that West must hold three clubs, unless everyone was playing a very deep game. If the opposition were to be believed the diamonds were 4–4, as West had led the two and East was in no hurry to cash the diamond winners. With a five-card spade suit West would surely have led one—thus she held no more than four. She was known to hold a doubleton heart, so must have at least three clubs. Easy when you direct you thoughts along the right lines.

The next hand features Mildred slipping from grace once more.

Game all
Dealer South

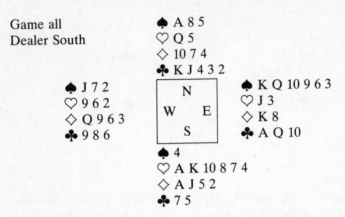

```
                    ♠ A 8 5
                    ♡ Q 5
                    ◇ 10 7 4
                    ♣ K J 4 3 2
  ♠ J 7 2              N          ♠ K Q 10 9 6 3
  ♡ 9 6 2                         ♡ J 3
  ◇ Q 9 6 3         W   E         ◇ K 8
  ♣ 9 8 6              S          ♣ A Q 10
                    ♠ 4
                    ♡ A K 10 8 7 4
                    ◇ A J 5 2
                    ♣ 7 5
```

The bidding:

S	W	N	E
(Daisy)	(A. A.)	(Gert)	(Mildred)
1 ♡	No	2 ♣	2 ♠
3 ♡	No	4 ♡	No
No	No		

Aunt Agatha led the two of spades to dummy's ace. At trick two Daisy played the four of diamonds, East following with the eight, declarer the knave and Aunt Agatha the queen. The spade continuation was ruffed by declarer, and a club to the knave and queen placed the lead with East. Having nothing obvious to do at this point Mildred played a low heart to declarer's ace. A second club was won by East, and the heart return was won by dummy's queen. A club ruff and a third round of trumps left Daisy with one final hurdle to negotiate. She cashed the ace of diamonds and when Mildred's king fell she claimed the remainder of the tricks.

'That was *so* lucky—my king of diamonds falling and giving you an entry to dummy,' observed Mildred, none too happily. 'Would it have been better if you had refused to take your queen of diamonds on the first round, partner?' she queried, almost apologetically.

'Of course not,' retorted Aunt Agatha, surprised that Mildred should even hint at the possibility that she, Aunt Agatha of all people, might have made a mistake. 'Any fool could make the contract after that defence. Cash the ace of diamonds and play another. The fourth diamond is ruffed with the queen of hearts. Trumps are then drawn, and when your knave falls declarer's problems are over.'

'Oh well, I'm glad we couldn't do any better,' said Mildred as they added up the score.

Aunt Agatha glowered, but, no doubt because she did not want the opposition to derive any pleasure from the knowledge that they could have been defeated, she remained silent—a Herculean task for my aunt at the best of times. She had obviously spotted the defensive errors. Have you?

THE LAST SAY

Mildred should have hopped up with the king of diamonds at trick two. That would have wrecked communications and left declarer without a satisfactory counter. If she fails to draw trumps, Mildred can get a ruff. If she does draw trumps, the defence must still prevail. Despite the general rule 'second player plays low, third player plays high'—a throwback to the days of whist—there are plenty of occasions when it is essential to contribute a high honour as second player. Such gambits mostly come under the heading of Disruptive Timing Plays, and East should have recognized that all the ingredients were present on this deal. Aunt Agatha herself was not completely foot perfect. She should have switched to a trump at trick three. That would have ditched declarer completely.

There was nobody waiting to cut in, so the same four drew again for partners. The outcome was far from promising: Aunt Agatha cut with Gert, 'The more butch of the two KGB agents,' as she put it, while Mildred was landed with Daisy.

After a few uneventful hands the cards fell like this:

Love all
Dealer East

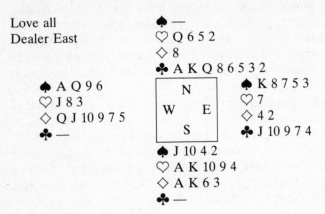

♠ —
♡ Q 6 5 2
♢ 8
♣ A K Q 8 6 5 3 2

♠ A Q 9 6
♡ J 8 3
♢ Q J 10 9 7 5
♣ —

♠ K 8 7 5 3
♡ 7
♢ 4 2
♣ J 10 9 7 4

♠ J 10 4 2
♡ A K 10 9 4
♢ A K 6 3
♣ —

The bidding:

S (Mildred)	W (Gert)	N (Daisy)	E (A. A.)
—	—	—	No
1 ♡	2 ♢	4 ♣	No
4 ♡	4 ♠	5 ♡	5 ♠
6 ♡	No	No	No

West led the ace of spades which was ruffed in dummy. A low club was ruffed with the four of hearts and overruffed by West. A second spade forced dummy again, but declarer quickly claimed the rest of the tricks: another low club was ruffed with the ace of trumps, and then the king and queen of trumps left dummy with tricks to burn.

'I thought we had underbid it,' observed Daisy, 'but with that horrible distribution twelve tricks is our limit.'

Mildred smiled approvingly but did not want to say too much for fear of provoking Aunt Agatha, who was looking anything but happy. Gert, however, had no such inhibitions.

'You had five spades to the king, partner, and wouldn't save in six spades,' she complained critically.

'Save what?' hissed Aunt Agatha menacingly, like a cobra poised to strike its victim in the vitals.

Mildred recognized the signs only too well and was glad that she had not fanned the flames with any observations of her own.

'Save against their cold slam, of course,' retorted Gert, surprised at her partner's apparent stupidity.

Aunt Agatha glared across the table, her eyes narrowing to small slits, but at first it seemed from her reply that she was full of contrition. However, the sting was in the tail.

'Yes, you are quite right. I should have saved—with you as a partner, on lead, and with about as much idea of defence as the man on the moon.'

I imagine that Gert was unfamiliar with this sort of attack but she showed no sign of flinching. However, the seeds of doubt, nurtured by Aunt Agatha's authoritative tone, must surely have taken root.

Aunt Agatha continued, interrupting Gert's attempt to vindicate herself. 'If you had had the wit to refrain from overruffing the club at trick two, which should have been obvious to a child, declarer would still be going down. Even a trump lead defeats the slam—providing you don't fall into the trap of overruffing.'

A heated argument continued for some time before the cards were dealt for the next hand, and while Mildred and Daisy were credited with the points on the score-sheet, it was Aunt Agatha who finally won the battle of the post mortem.

THE LAST SAY

Aunt Agatha's analysis was spot-on. Six spades would not have been a classic success, and six hearts was easily defeatable. The club distribution was known to West immediately, and it should have been easy to see what would happen if she overruffed.

Perhaps West should have asked herself this simple question: 'Is there any chance of the contract succeeding without bringing in the club suit?' The answer, 'None', would surely flash out loud and clear, and from that moment onwards she could approach her problem with single-mindedness. Maybe it was not quite clear what would happen if she discarded on the club, but eclipsing the dummy should have been the top priority. Nature could then take its course.

Every bridge-player has his (or her) moment. A lucky contract, maybe; a present from considerate opponents; an inspired view. Even the most modest performer will occasionally record a spectacular success, dine out on it for months to come and forget a thousand errors as the memory of the coup obliterates less pleasing episodes from the mind. Mildred experienced such a success when she held the following hand as East:

E–W game
Dealer South

♠ K Q 7
♡ A 8
◇ Q 6 4
♣ K J 9 8 6

♠ 9 8
♡ K 9 6
◇ J 5 2
♣ A 7 4 3 2

The bidding:

S	N
(Gert)	(A. A.)
1 NT*	3 NT
* *12–14*	

Daisy, West led the two of hearts. What did Mildred know that the others didn't, and how should she defend if declarer plays a low heart from dummy?

This was the full hand:

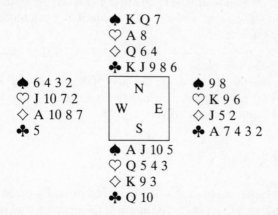

```
              ♠ K Q 7
              ♡ A 8
              ◇ Q 6 4
              ♣ K J 9 8 6
  ♠ 6 4 3 2        N         ♠ 9 8
  ♡ J 10 7 2                 ♡ K 9 6
  ◇ A 10 8 7   W       E     ◇ J 5 2
  ♣ 5              S         ♣ A 7 4 3 2
              ♠ A J 10 5
              ♡ Q 5 4 3
              ◇ K 9 3
              ♣ Q 10
```

'You'll no doubt realize, Freddie,' confided Mildred, giving me her own version of the deal, 'I don't often get a very good count of the hand,' (she means she rarely bothers to count at all) 'but on this occasion I knew the exact shape of everyone's hand immediately dummy was exposed. My partner's lead indicated a four-card suit, and she would obviously have led from a five-timer if she had one. With five clubs in dummy and two marked in declarer's hand (South could not hold three clubs, because that would have left West with a void and therefore at least one five-card suit), West must hold a singleton—so her shape was precisely 4–4–4–1. With that information available to me I judged it just right when declarer played a low heart from dummy. I won with my king and played a low diamond. Daisy allowed dummy to win, but then when I regained the lead with the ace of clubs I played the knave of diamonds, so declarer lost three diamonds, one heart and one club.'

Bravo, Mildred! Good card-reading and well judged, I say. Daisy was marked with a maximum of five points, so could hardly hold the queen of hearts *and* the ace of diamonds; a heart return at trick two was unlikely to be good enough.

The fact that Gert did not judge the hand as well as Mildred did not go by unnoticed. Gert was none too happy about her own performance and perhaps in an effort to pre-empt Aunt Agatha she said, 'Damn it! I could have made it if I'd gone up with dummy's ace of hearts.'

'Twice,' observed Aunt Agatha enigmatically.

'What do you mean, twice?'

'You could have put up the ace of hearts or the king of diamonds and succeeded in either case. That's twice,' added Aunt Agatha unnecessarily.

THE LAST SAY

It sometimes happens that declarer can virtually place all the outstanding honour cards the moment the opening lead is made. The bidding—or lack of it—and the card chosen for the attack provide such a vivid picture that filling in the remaining gaps by inference is quite simple. However, it is rare for a defender to be able to get such an accurate distributional count at trick one, and almost without precedent for Mildred to be cast in that role. While Mildred deserved all the praise she got, I'm inclined to think that Gert deserved some sympathy. She didn't really do anything obviously wrong. She was unlucky to experience Mildred suddenly playing and thinking well above her natural handicap mark, and the lie of the cards could not have been more perverse.

Perhaps the last hand rattled Gert somewhat, and no doubt Aunt Agatha's caustic comments didn't help. In any case Gert seemed to lose her concentration when she ran into a bad break on the following hand.

E–W game
Dealer North

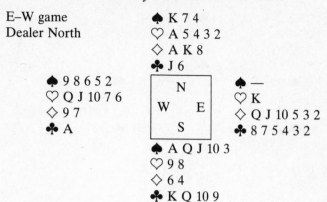

♠ K 7 4
♡ A 5 4 3 2
♢ A K 8
♣ J 6

♠ 9 8 6 5 2
♡ Q J 10 7 6
♢ 9 7
♣ A

```
        N
   W         E
        S
```

♠ —
♡ K
♢ Q J 10 5 3 2
♣ 8 7 5 4 3 2

♠ A Q J 10 3
♡ 9 8
♢ 6 4
♣ K Q 10 9

The bidding:

S	W	N	E
(Gert)	(Daisy)	(A. A.)	(Mildred)
—	—	1 ♡	No
1 ♠	No	2 ♠	2 NT
4 ♠	No	No	No

West led the queen of hearts, East's king falling under
dummy's ace. A trump to the queen revealed the bad news. It
was clear that Gert could not yet draw trumps and that the ace of
clubs had to be knocked out as an early priority. So trick three
went to the ace of clubs, and then a heart winner was followed by
another heart. Declarer ruffed and, still unable to draw trumps,
played a second club. West ruffed (her third trick) and continued
with yet another heart. South ruffed, leaving this position:

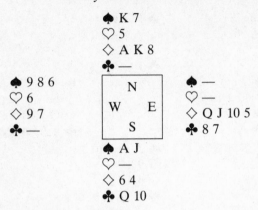

```
            ♠ K 7
            ♡ 5
            ◇ A K 8
            ♣ —
♠ 9 8 6                        ♠ —
♡ 6                            ♡ —
◇ 9 7                          ◇ Q J 10 5
♣ —                            ♣ 8 7
            ♠ A J
            ♡ —
            ◇ 6 4
            ♣ Q 10
```

No matter how declarer played she could not prevent Daisy from making one more trump trick. Gert did her best at this point by playing clubs, but Daisy simply discarded diamonds and waited for the inevitable. One down.

'That was a really vicious break,' complained Gert. 'Desperately unlucky.'

'Nothing to do with luck,' snorted Aunt Agatha. 'You were handed a barrel-load of luck on a platter and refused to use it. First of all you could have doubled Mildred's unusual two notrumps. Any contract played by them would have cost a small fortune. Then you could—and should—have cashed the ace of diamonds early on in your own contract, in which case you would have sailed home.'

Odd though it may seem, Aunt Agatha's observations about the diamond trick were quite correct. Take the ace of diamonds away from the North hand and a small one from each of the other hands and the position becomes:

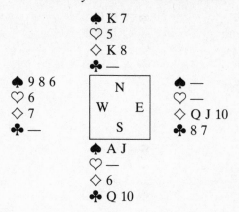

```
              ♠ K 7
              ♡ 5
              ◇ K 8
              ♣ —
♠ 9 8 6      ┌─────────┐      ♠ —
♡ 6          │    N    │      ♡ —
◇ 7          │ W     E │      ◇ Q J 10
♣ —          │    S    │      ♣ 8 7
             └─────────┘
              ♠ A J
              ♡ —
              ◇ 6
              ♣ Q 10
```

On the queen of clubs, West and dummy discard diamonds. When the ten of clubs follows, West is left without further resource.

THE LAST SAY

The position in which Gert found herself is not greatly dissimilar to that of a declarer who is about to embark on a crossruff. On these occasions it is usually best to cash the side-winners before actually starting the ruffs. This lessens the risk of a defender being able to trump one of declarer's high cards later in the game. Had Gert counted her winners—five spades, one heart and three clubs—she would have realized that she needed one diamond trick for her contract, and this could have been taken at trick three. In the event she could have cashed two diamond tricks, although no real advantage would have accrued from the second.

The next two hands spotlight Aunt Agatha in a more familiar role. As she put it herself: 'I was in complete command, and played brilliantly. I just had to polish off the rubber and get away from that table and those dreadful females.'

E–W game
Dealer South

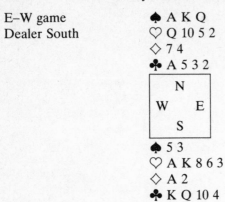

♠ A K Q
♥ Q 10 5 2
♦ 7 4
♣ A 5 3 2

♠ 5 3
♥ A K 8 6 3
♦ A 2
♣ K Q 10 4

The bidding:

S	W	N	E
(A. A.)	(Mildred)	(Gert)	(Daisy)
1 ♥	No	2 ♣	No
4 ♣	No	4 ♠	No
5 ♦	No	6 ♥	No
No	No		

West leads the king of diamonds. How should declarer plan the play?

The task looks simple enough, but Aunt Agatha gave the hand very careful consideration before committing herself at trick one. Then, having formed her plan, she won the ace of diamonds and played a low heart to dummy's queen. West showed void of trumps but Aunt Agatha's pips were just good enough to pick up East's J 9 7 4. The diamond loser disappeared on dummy's third spade, but a club had to be lost to West who held J 9 8 7. Contract made. This was the full deal: